Health Care in the United Kingdom

By Allan Grieve, Sandy McCann and John MacTaggart

Imprint
publishing systems

Imprint Publishing Systems Limited,
59 Colvilles Place,
Kelvin Industrial Estate,
East Kilbride,
G75 0PZ.

Published by Imprint Publishing Systems Limited 2000

Copyright © Imprint Publishing Systems Limited 2000

Written by Allan Grieve, Sandy McCann and John MacTaggart.

ISBN 1 872 035 80 9

Editors Harry Blee, Graham Dalglish and Jim McGregor.
Designed by Kenneth Maskrey.

Printed by J. S. Burns & Sons, Glasgow.

Contents

The National Health Service in Perspective

Inequalities in Health

The Politics of Health

Acknowledgement

Images used on pages
57, 59, 60, 61, 64, 66, 72, 73, 74, 81, 87, 92, 96, 116
are licensed under copyright from PhotoDisc

The National Health Service in Perspective

Introduction

The creation of the National Health Service (NHS) in 1948 was a genuine landmark in the development of British society. It was the first time that a health service which was comprehensive and national in scope had been created anywhere in the world. Although British society has changed a great deal since then and the questions facing health care in the new millennium are to some extent different, the fundamental challenges remain the same as they were in 1948.

There is the significant economic problem of finding resources to meet demand for health care. Governments must make choices between different competing demands for finance. Certain critics of government policy argue that some of the money currently spent on health should be reallocated to other areas of public provision such as education, housing or defence.

There are also social issues to be considered. The structure of British society is very different today from that which existed in 1948, e.g., many more people now have a larger disposable income and are willing to avoid waiting lists and enjoy greater comfort. Despite the existence of a national health service, some commentators recognise that there remain wide and growing disparities in health between the social classes.

The economic and social issues referred to above have generated political debate. For example, to what extent should the state provide health care and individuals be expected to look after themselves and their families? What role, if any, should the private and voluntary sectors play in modern health care?

However, the context within which this political debate takes place has changed. The NHS was formed at a time when state socialism was a very important ideology in Britain. In practical terms, this meant that the state would have the main role in providing important services with some limited private and voluntary sector involvement tolerated. However, by the 1980s, while the British public continued to support the objectives of the NHS, the values of individualism and capitalism had taken an increasing hold within British society.

In the new millennium, the consensus is that there should be a state-run health service but one which works in partnership with the private and voluntary sectors. This is sometimes described as the 'Third Way'. Increasingly, the individual has responsibility for his or her own health but the state is there to provide for the weakest members of society.

STUDY TOPIC 1

What factors led to the creation of the National Health Service?

"You had to hand over the money before he'd even examine you. We couldn't afford it. That was five shillings worth of bread, milk and potatoes we didn't have. A doctor's bill meant we went hungry."

(Charlie Everett, 72, recalls the days before the NHS, The Herald 12 August 1999)

Towards State Intervention

The National Health Service came into existence on 'Vesting Day', July 5 1948. Before that, British society reflected laissez-faire capitalism, with little social security or health provision for the poor. Indeed, there was the dominant belief that the poor had only themselves to blame for their plight. The fact that people had to endure pain and unnecessary death because they could not afford treatment made little impact on government policy. Commenting on the events of 'Vesting Day', Dr John Marks, noted:

"There was a colossal amount of unmet need that just poured in. There were women with prolapsed uteruses literally wobbling down their legs. It was the same with hernias. You would have men walking around with trusses holding colossal hernias in. They were like that because they couldn't afford to have it done."

The origins of the NHS can be traced as far back as the 1911 National Insurance Act of Liberal Chancellor, Lloyd George. Workers paid 4p per week in National Insurance contributions; the employer 3p and the Government 2p. In return for this, a doctor was provided for all male workers who earned under £160 a year (average earnings at the time). However, according to Malcolm Dean of The Guardian, this was a limited response: *"The principle of the 1911 Insurance Act was plain enough: get the workers back to work, but don't worry about the wives and children."*

While the Act, in hindsight, was hardly comprehensive, it was a clever piece of politics. It eased the consciences of the middle classes who felt guilty about the plight of the poor. It put clear political water between the Liberals and the Conservatives. Also, it reduced the impact of more radical demands from the socialist movement for greater state help. The 1911 National Insurance Act was the first ever admission by a British Government that it had a responsibility to provide health care for those who could not afford to pay.

Lloyd George

© CORBIS/ Hulton-Deutsch Collection

Private, Voluntary and Municipal Hospitals

Before 1948, there were three types of hospitals: private, voluntary and municipal. The private hospitals were used by the rich and the middle classes. While medical science was not as advanced as it is now, standards for those able to pay were as good as those existing anywhere in the world. The voluntary hospitals survived largely through fundraising and charitable donations. Only the 'fortunate' poor were treated in voluntary hospitals. Some doctors were willing to work in voluntary hospitals without payment. They earned a living by continuing to charge private patients who could afford to pay. This allowed those doctors to continue donating their services to the voluntary sector.

However, many people had to take their chances in the municipal hospitals of the big cities. The municipal hospitals were often former workhouses and were viewed as menacing places which people were frightened to enter. There was some justification for this attitude, doctors were in short supply and nurses poorly trained. There were few drugs and anaesthetics were rarely available. The mentally handicapped and mentally ill were often locked away and forgotten about. Standards of hygiene were described as deplorable.

The historian, Geoffrey Rivett, described horrific conditions in Paddington General hospital where the legs of cots in the maternity ward had to be placed in tins of oil to stop the spread of cockroaches. The threat of infectious disease taking hold within such hospitals was real. Diseases such as diphtheria, smallpox, scarlet fever and whooping cough, all of which are rare in Britain today, were killers at the beginning of the 20th century. As recently as 1948, tuberculosis (TB) killed 23,000 people in the United Kingdom (UK).

The rich, meanwhile, could afford to pay for the services of private medicine and hospital treatment. Many felt that this social class inequality in health care provision was

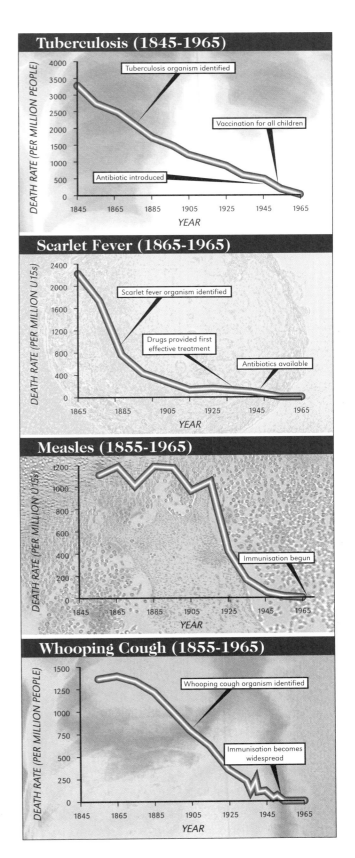

wrong, indeed immoral. However, it took the Second World War, and the state-run medical provision existent at that time to convince the Government that a national health service could be established and that this would raise standards of health care for all.

The Five Giant Evils

The Liberal, Sir William Beveridge, had been appointed by the wartime coalition Government to examine how public services could be provided after the war. Beveridge's all-party committee was a product of the 'collectivist' spirit within British society at that time. All classes in society had endured suffering and loss. Cities had been bombed and blitzed. As working class children were evacuated to the countryside, middle class people who had previously thought of the poor as dirty and uncivilised, discovered that they were, in fact, ordinary human beings with the same hopes and fears as wealthier people. Many were shocked by the living conditions the urban poor endured and supported state efforts to create a more equal society.

There was a political mood, reflected in the huge vote given to the 1945 Labour Government, which expressed the desire to rebuild Britain collectively in order to reduce, if not eradicate, the social class divisions in British society. The 1945 Labour Government adopted an explicitly 'collectivist' ideology towards society in an attempt to socially engineer a New Britain. No longer would government adopt a 'laissez-faire' approach to the economy and society.

Beveridge had identified five 'giant evils' of society: *"Squalor, idleness, ignorance, want and disease"*. To combat the evil of 'squalor', a programme of council house building was started. Slum houses in the big cities were demolished and replaced by houses with affordable rents in new schemes. Plans were made for ambitious new towns such as Cumbernauld, East Kilbride, Glenrothes, Irvine and Livingston to ease overcrowding and improve the environment. The demand for construction and other workers which this generated acted to reduce 'idleness'.

Idleness was also tackled through 'nationalisation'. A large number of privately owned industries were nationalised and run by the Government, not for private profit, but 'for the people'. Coal, gas, steel, airways and telecommunications became state owned.

The Liberal, Sir William Beveridge

Other private employers such as Rolls Royce, which ran into financial trouble, were taken over by the Government to save jobs 'for the public good'.

In education, the objective was to end the unpopular '11 Plus' school examination. Once this had been achieved, children would no longer be required to attend separate secondary schools on the basis of results provided by a single exam. The intention was that to end 'ignorance', pupils would attend the new comprehensive schools which were being developed. With this approach, it was hoped that state schools would become so good that better off parents would see no benefit in choosing the private sector.

The idea of 'social security' was developed. The Government would, through general taxation of the working population, take responsibility for the welfare of the public thereby eliminating 'want'. It was believed that with most people working, taxes could be paid to look after those unable to work. The consensus was that new 'Keynesian' economic policies would make mass unemployment a thing of the past.

In summary, the 1945 Labour Government had created what has now become known as the 'Welfare State' with the idea of care 'from the cradle to the grave'. The last remaining evil, 'disease', was to be tackled by its 'jewel in the crown', the new National Health Service. No longer would health needs be left to the financial status of the individual or the workings of the free market. The state would provide.

The Collectivist Consensus

While Beveridge's 1944 Health White Paper made no specific references as to how the new NHS should be organised, its three main aims were clear:

1. *"Everybody, irrespective of means, age, sex or occupation shall have the opportunity to benefit from the best and most up-to-date medical services available."*

2. *"The service would be 'comprehensive' and 'free of charge' for those wishing to take advantage of it."*

3. *"It would promote good health, 'rather than only the treatment of bad'."*

All the major political parties agreed with this basic consensus. As the Glasgow Herald commented at the time: *"Though the socialists may be expected to take full credit for introducing an extensive social security system, they are building on foundations laid by the coalition government"*.

Shaping the NHS

"Administration will be the chief headache for years to come."
Aneurin Bevan

While the all-party Beveridge report recommended that the NHS be established, it was Aneurin Bevan as Minister of Health who gave the NHS its distinctive shape. In order to convince the many talented doctors and dentists, who made large salaries treating only the rich, Bevan allowed them to keep their private clients if they agreed to work in the NHS. Patients would continue to have the right to choose to be treated privately. Indeed, private wards and 'pay beds' would be available within NHS hospitals. Bevan also decided that the only way the service would be improved was for it to be funded by income tax, rather than by national insurance. Today, 86% of NHS funding comes from income tax, 12% from national insurance and 2% from charges.

The main political parties agreed on the basic principles of the NHS. It should be a comprehensive service, caring for all and free at the point of use. The first political row blew up when the Conservative Party defended the rights of the private practising general practitioners (GPs) who wished to continue working privately outwith the NHS. The Conservatives also defended the rights of certain voluntary hospitals which wished to remain independent and resisted nationalisation. Bevan's anger at this development was reflected by his comment that those Conservatives were *"lower than vermin"*.

Aneurin Bevan

STUDY TOPIC 2

To what extent does the responsibility for health care lie with the state or the individual?

Health - An Important Political and Economic Issue

All of the main parties now place great importance on health as a political and economic issue and their election manifestos reflect this, as does the quantity, if not quality, of debate between the parties during and between election campaigns.

There are many pressure and interest groups which relate to health provision and consumption. These range from trade unions and professional associations (which promote policies for the NHS and private health care as well as attempting to protect the interests of their members) to charities with specific areas of interest over which they try to exert influence.

At its inception in 1948, the NHS was a political issue which divided the two main parties. The post-war Labour Government's proposals met with opposition from the Conservative Party, even though these were based on a consensus established by all parties in the wartime coalition government.

Significantly, the NHS also met with initial opposition from the British Medical Association (BMA), which represents doctors. Nowadays, all of the main British and Scottish political parties support the NHS (as does the BMA and a range of other NHS trade unions and professional associations).

At present, differences between the parties relate more to the administration of the NHS and to differing emphases on aspects of health care, rather than to ideological or qualitative differences over whether the NHS should exist in the first place. The fact that the NHS is supported by all of the main parties and survived the significant ideological upheaval of the 'Thatcher revolution' of the 1980s is an indication of how highly it is regarded by the British people. Accordingly, all of the main parties appear to regard the NHS as a national institution whose existence is beyond question.

Responsibility for Health: The State or the Individual?

Typical Comparative Costs for Different Treatments	
Coronary Bypass Graft Operation	£7,500 per case
Renal Dialysis	£22,420 per year
Kidney Transplant Operation	£18,580 per case
Adult Intensive Care	£1,200 per day
Baby in a Special Care Baby Unit	£1,000 per day

Given the poor standards of health for the vast majority of the public in the pre-war years, few people would today deny the need for NHS provision. Equally, few would deny the tremendous advances made in health care within the UK during the NHS era. The NHS remains a popular British institution, and politicians across the political spectrum are very aware of that fact.

Collectivists would claim that it is the collectivist ethos of the NHS that constitutes its main strength. There is no doubt that the service has fostered a tremendous degree of goodwill and staff loyalty. Many doctors and nurses work beyond their contractual duties precisely because the service is non-profit-making. According to the consumer magazine, *Which* (July 1998), international comparisons show that spending on healthcare is lower in the UK than in other advanced countries such as the USA, France or Germany. A significant amount of US expenditure on health is financed by individual members of the public in order to pay for many services provided free of charge in Britain by the NHS. The key issue is the extent to which the state or the individual can most effectively tackle bad health. The new killers of today, e.g., coronary heart disease and lung cancer, are linked to an unhealthy lifestyle. Is this an individual choice, and therefore the individual's responsibility? Or are unhealthy lifestyles the result of wider social problems, and therefore a government responsibility?

International Comparisons

When total spending on health care in the UK is compared with that of other developed countries it can be seen that the proportion of its GDP which the UK devotes to health care is comparatively low.

Health Spending in Selected Countries (% of GDP)

Column 1: *Total Health Spending in Selected Countries
Column 2 : Health Spending by Governments in Selected Countries (in brackets)

	Country	Column 1	Column 2
	USA	14.3	(6.3)
	Austria	9.8	(6.2)
	France	9.8	(7.7)
	Germany	9.6	(6.8)
	Netherlands	8.5	(6.8)
	Finland	8.4	(6.2)
	Italy	8.4	(5.9)
	Belgium	8.2	(7.1)
	Ireland	8.0	(7.0)
	Sweden	7.8	(6.4)
	Portugal	7.7	(4.2)
	Spain	7.1	(5.7)
	UK	7.0	(5.8)
	Denmark	6.6	(5.6)
	Greece	5.1	(3.2)

Source: Compendium of Health Statistics, 1997

* Total health spending includes government spending and that made by individual consumers on private medical insurance, dental care, optical care and prescriptions.

United States of America

250	National Population (millions)
16.7	Birth Rate (per 1000 population)
72.0 male 78.8 female	Life Expectancy at Birth (years)
9.2 male 8.4 female	Death Rate (per 1000 population)

Description of Health Service

- Private providers deliver health care for most people.
- Government funded health care available to needy groups.
- 3 out of 4 people approximately opt for private health care.

United Kingdom

57.4	National Population (millions)
13.9	Birth Rate (per 1000 population)
73.1 male 78.5 female	Life Expectancy at Birth (years)
11.2	Death Rate (per 1000 population)

Description of Health Service

- NHS services free at point of use and funded from tax revenue.
- Emergency treatment available at local hospitals.
- 1 in 10 people approximately opt for private health care.

Source: Guide to Health Services of the World (1990)

In the list shown above, only two countries have lower total expenditure (in terms of percentage of GDP) than the UK and only four have less government expenditure (in terms of percentage of GDP). It is notable that in the USA, where the majority of health care is funded through private insurance, government expenditure (in terms of percentage of GDP) is higher than in the UK, 6.3% compared to 5.8%.

Collectivists v Individualists

Collectivists take the view that the NHS cannot promote good health in isolation. Good housing, education, employment and a balanced diet are all important to an individual's health. Collectivists believe that there is a strong link between poverty and ill health and that, ultimately, promoting good health is beyond the limited scope of the NHS. They contend that the Government must work in partnership with the NHS to narrow inequalities in those other respects as social deprivation breeds ill health.

The housing scheme of Drumchapel in Glasgow, for example, has one of the lowest car ownership ratios in Scotland. Nevertheless, it has one of the highest car-related death statistics. According to Dr Harry Burns, Director of Public Health for Greater Glasgow, the answer does not necessarily lie in improving Accident and Emergency facilities, but in installing 'sleeping policemen' on roads. Areas with significant social deprivation also have higher instances of heart and lung disease. This is often reflected by differences in life expectancy. For example, according to some surveys, the difference in average life expectancy between Drumchapel and its affluent neighbour, Bearsden, is as much as ten years.

While smoking, alcohol and drug addiction are contributory factors to illness, collectivists do not believe in 'blaming the individual'. Instead, they point to the social and economic pressures of unemployment and bleak housing which create a demand for the 'escapes' of cigarettes, alcohol and drugs.

A contrasting viewpoint is held by individualists. This view was influential during the Conservative years of 1979-1997. According to this perspective, the individual not the state, should take primary responsibility for health and individuals should make 'healthy lifestyle' choices. While individualists concede that there may be pressures to be unhealthy, they do not accept that people can blame outside forces for destructive habits. They argue that, given the

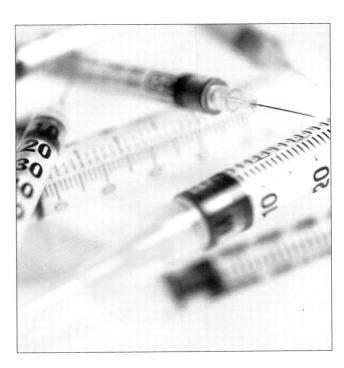

Risk of Death in One Year	
Injecting illegal drugs	1 in 50
Smoking ten cigarettes a day	1 in 200
Mountain climbing	1 in 1,500
Driving a car	1 in 8,000
Playing soccer	1 in 25,000

strong preventive health measures adopted by government in recent years in relation to the dangers of smoking and the value of healthy lifestyles, individuals are aware of the risks. It is estimated, for example, that households in the lowest tenth of the income range spend more than £500 per year on tobacco. The taxpayer, therefore, should not be forced to 'pick up the tab' for this undesirable habit. Individualists believe that the post war 'nanny state' has created a generation which fails to take responsibility for its own health. They would be in favour of allowing individuals to 'opt out' of paying taxes for the NHS with this being replaced by private medical insurance (PMI) cover designed to address their own particular health needs. The role of government, it is argued, should be one of informing people of their lifestyle choices and the consequences of their actions.

Collectivism and Individualism - 'The Third Way'

The new Labour Government has attempted to reconcile both points of view. It has taken the step of explicitly acknowledging the link, denied by governments for almost twenty years, between poverty and ill health. In tackling this problem, it aims to improve housing, enhance educational standards and encourage people to move from 'welfare to work'. These changes are viewed as having a long term impact but increasingly 'public health' rather than hospital-based solutions is seen as the answer.

At the same time, the Government has adopted strong health promotion measures to promote taking exercise and a healthier diet. According to the Government, the NHS is there to help but individuals have to play their part too. The Conservative Party has also recognised that 'the environment that people live in affects their health'. Ultimately, prevention is better and cheaper than cure.

Private Medical Insurance

The number of people with private medical insurance (PMI) has grown significantly. At present, 12.7% of the population are covered compared with less than 2% in 1948. The biggest increase occurred in the 1980s. This was, in part, a reflection of the fears of some people that the NHS might no longer be able to meet their health needs or those of their families. It was also a response to the political culture of the time, when individual responsibility was a dominant theme of 'Thatcherism'. At that time, the Government allowed retired people to claim tax relief on contributions to PMI and that accounted for some of the increase. The numbers with PMI reached a peak in 1990 and has remained steady since. Fully 40% of those with PMI have personal plans, while the rest are covered through company schemes.

Provision of Dental Treatment

A survey by the Consumers' Association in 1997 found that 53% of dentists no longer take on new NHS patients - a result principally of cuts in funding of dental care by the Government. It is significant that the White Paper for England and Wales on the NHS entitled, "The New NHS: Modern, Dependable." published by the Labour Government in 1997, made no mention of dental care. However, the Scottish Office did announce, in 1998, that it was to allocate £1 million to help increase the provision of NHS dental treatment in Scotland. This is, perhaps, an indication of how priorities for the two nations may vary under a Scottish Parliament.

Future Options

It seems very unlikely that, in Britain (or in a devolved or independent Scotland), the principle of a health service free at the point of delivery would ever be replaced by one where the individual citizen assumes total responsibility for paying for his or her health care. The NHS has become so entrenched as a national institution that it would be difficult politically for any political party to propose its abolition.

However, there are some examples of health provision, previously free at the point of demand but now subject to charges, which have changed without causing too much political upset. Prescription charges are now accepted as inevitable by the 20% of the UK population who have to pay them.

The near disappearance of free dental and optical care for most of the population has been met by expressions of regret rather than outrage. Also, the creeping privatisation of nursing and residential care for the elderly and the requirement that some of its costs be paid for by the patient has caused some controversy and is the subject of a Royal Commission, but it was never an issue to make people take to the streets in protest, let alone become pivotal in an election campaign.

Possibly, experience of those changes and the relatively low-key reaction to them, could give future governments cause to consider other options for charges, e.g., they could be extended to cover most prescriptions, all dental and optical care or accommodation charges for hospital stays. If such charges were to become accepted, more and more NHS services might be considered legitimate targets for charging.

One further option which could take the responsibility for funding health care away from the state and place an increasing onus on individual citizens is that of making private medical insurance compulsory with some tax relief on the premiums. Under such circumstances, individuals would insure themselves against ill-health as they might take out warranties against the breakdown of a car or an electrical appliance. The insurance company would meet the bill for medical care as required.

In this way, individuals' health care needs would be met with a reduced requirement for public funding. However, it is possible that a significant number of people might still have to be catered for by the state. This is likely to include those too poor to pay insurance premiums and those with chronic conditions or alcohol and drug-related conditions which insurance companies refuse to cover at present.

It is significant that the Conservative Government rejected the option of moving significantly towards private medical insurance as the means of funding health care in 1988 on the basis that it would give insurance companies and private health providers too much power to decide clinical priorities. Also, the Conservative Government of that time concluded that under such circumstances premiums were likely to rise leading to increasing inflation.

STUDY TOPIC 3

Why is the provision of the National Health Service so important economically?

Managing the Economic Dimension

The importance of the NHS as a political issue extends beyond party politics and elections. It is about managing effectively a huge amount of resources and an extremely large and important UK industry. The range and scale of its workforce has given rise to some very important and articulate pressure groups. There are many interest groups involved in the provision of health care, the formulation of health care policies and the protection of the interests of those employed in the NHS.

The range of skills necessary to provide health care and the number of related activities requiring employment of workers necessitates a large number of employees with diverse skills and expertise. The statistics below illustrate this fact.

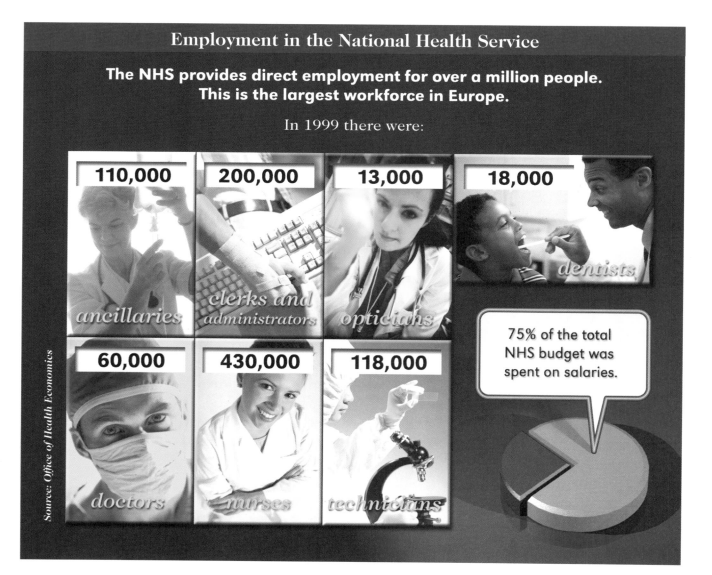

Employment in the National Health Service

The NHS provides direct employment for over a million people. This is the largest workforce in Europe.

In 1999 there were:

110,000 — ancillaries

200,000 — clerks and administrators

13,000 — opticians

18,000 — dentists

60,000 — doctors

430,000 — nurses

118,000 — technicians

75% of the total NHS budget was spent on salaries.

Source: Office of Health Economics

A week in the life of the NHS

Did you know that in a typical week?

- more than 800,000 people will be treated in hospital out-patient clinics; about 700,000 will visit the dentist for a check-up; pharmacists will dispense around 8.5m items on prescription; and over 100,000 babies will be delivered;

- in the country's 300 or so general hospitals, surgeons will perform around 1,200 hip operations. Ambulances will make over 50,000 emergency journeys and around 50,000 people will donate blood;

- in the community, around 1.4m people will receive help in their home from the NHS; district nurses will make more than 700,000 visits; and chiropodists will provide around 150,000 sessions.

All of these groups of employees, although obviously concerned with the provision of health care, are also, understandably, concerned with promoting their own professional and economic interests within the NHS. They have various trade unions and professional associations to perform this function collectively on their behalf.

The scope of the provision made by the NHS and its contribution to the nation's health is indicated by the following statistics. At present, there are 270,000 beds in hospitals, occupied daily, on average, by 227,000 patients. In a typical year, six million patients are treated by consultants (two million patients are over sixty five and one million under four years of age). The most common medical treatments relate to: pregnancies (1.1 million), digestive disorders (1 million) and circulation problems (928,000).

Surgeons perform 5.7 million operations in a typical year. Of these, the most common are for the womb and female genital tract (599,000), bones and joints (482,000) and the stomach (471,000).

There are, in a typical year, 67 million appointments at out-patient departments. There are 295 million visits in a typical year to family doctors' surgeries (16 million in Scotland). In addition, 12,000 pharmacists nationwide dispense 560 million prescriptions (57 million in Scotland). The total value of these prescriptions, in 1998, was £5 billion pounds. Emergency services are also to the fore with ambulances making 2.7 million journeys in a typical year.

The NHS also provides 630,000 places in day care centres, 307,900 in residential care homes, 131,700 places in nursing homes and 73,600 places in dual registered homes. It sends 760,000 meals to residential homes or luncheon clubs.

The contribution that the NHS makes in Scotland is similarly impressive. In Scotland alone, NHS spending was £4.6 billion in 1997-98. This accounted for one third of total government expenditure in Scotland. A total of 135,000 people were employed in Scotland by the NHS. This figure was 10% more than in 1988 and constituted 5.9% of the Scottish workforce.

Servicing the Wider Economy

The range and scale of these activities not only provide direct employment in the NHS, but require supply and servicing from other industries outwith the NHS. The link with the NHS is obvious in some cases, but less so in others. For example, the supply of medicines from the pharmaceutical industry demonstrates the clear link between the NHS and an outside industry. This industry is an employer of well-qualified and highly skilled workers and is dependent on the NHS for its wellbeing and, indeed, its survival. As has been noted above, prescription expenditure in 1998 accounted for fully £5 billion.

The British pharmaceutical industry is regarded internationally as the world leader in its field. Many of its goods are exported, underlining its importance to the national economy. Pharmaceuticals is an example of a British industry which remains successful but relies on a government service for its continuing prosperity. The removal of the NHS, for whatever reason, would be a disaster for the industry. The various Health Departments in Scotland, England, Wales and Northern Ireland, therefore, are responsible not only for the NHS but for keeping the pharmaceutical industry in its leading position.

In addition, the NHS supports the construction industry. There is a continuing need for new NHS buildings to be constructed and for existing NHS properties to be maintained. Furthermore, the NHS spends an impressive £450 million each year on research and development.

Less obviously dependent on the NHS are industries that supply equipment and provide services relating to the day-to-day administration of the NHS, particularly hospitals. British Telecom, for example, provides telecommunications equipment and telephone services to hospitals, clinics and surgeries. Computer suppliers provide and service hardware and relevant software. Car manufacturers and sales and leasing companies supply and service vehicles. The list is extensive.

Servicing the Local Economy

The NHS can also be a major player in the local economy. There are some areas of the country, particularly inner cities, where the NHS is the major employer and the most significant focus of economic activity. Not only those directly employed in the NHS rely on it for employment, but small, local firms, which supply furniture, stationery and other goods and provide services like decorating or small-scale electrical repairs, may have the NHS as their principal or sole customer and the extent of their involvement with the NHS will directly determine the size of their workforce.

This is why the proposed closure of a hospital can become a vital community issue in such areas. Concern in those areas relates not only to the possible loss of a local health facility. The loss of a major employer, possibly the hub of the local economy, is another source of great concern for the immediate community. In addition, of course, the scale of NHS employment is such that concern will stretch beyond the community in which the hospital is situated. For example, the well-being of Stobhill and Canniesburn Hospitals and Glasgow Royal Infirmary is of importance in health care and employment terms not only to the residents of the particular areas within the City of Glasgow in which they are situated, but also to those living in neighbouring suburbs like Bishopbriggs, Bearsden and Milngavie.

Wages, Policy Initiatives and the Need for Bigger Budgets

Approximately, 75% of the NHS budget is devoted to paying the salaries of employees. Although many NHS employees are poorly paid, they have, at times, received pay rises that have been higher than the existing rate of inflation. It has often been the case that such pay rises have not been fully funded when governments have allocated the NHS budget. This has represented an additional burden for the NHS.

Also, more money has had to be found to discharge the commitments made by government policies and initiatives. Recent examples are community care and the battle against AIDS. This has constituted a further drain on the NHS budget.

In 1988, a Report of the House of Commons Select Committee on Social Services calculated that an increase of 2% per annum in real terms, taking into account price inflation that applied to items purchased by the NHS, was needed for the NHS to meet increasing demands. In fact, the increase in

spending by Conservative Governments from 1979 to 1986 accounted for a rise, in real terms, of only 1.7% per annum on average. This was 0.3% less than the recommended level.

More Efficient Management

The Conservative Government of that time recognised that 2% per annum in real terms was needed. However, it contended that this could be met from changes within the NHS and did not require additional funding from the public purse. The Government pointed out that more patients were being treated at a faster rate than ever before and claimed that this showed that productivity in the NHS was increasing. Also, it claimed that efficiency savings through compulsory, competitive tendering, the closure of smaller hospitals and better purchasing methods had led to existing funding being increasingly directed towards patient care.

Nevertheless, the Select Committee and other experts were of the opinion that, even taking such developments into account, the NHS had still been underfunded by £1,900 million over an eight year period (1979-1986).

This controversy over funding led eventually to the Government's reforms of the NHS which are discussed later. However, it should be noted that, throughout this controversy and also its whole period in office (1979-1997), the Conservative Party did provide expenditure increases which were significantly above the average rate of inflation. Also, the existence of the NHS was never once called into question, despite criticisms made of government management of the NHS. This contrasted with the ideological climate which existed at that time of 'rolling back' the state, privatisations and cuts in other public services. That the NHS survived under such circumstances is evidence of its resilience as a national institution.

A challenge for all governments in dealing with the NHS is the rising expectations of the general public. The growing demand for care, the cost of new technology and the development of new and expensive drugs to treat medical conditions have meant that, by 1997, it was agreed that an increase, in real terms, of 3% per annum would now be required to ensure that the NHS was adequately funded.

Furthermore, the impact of growing public expectations is unlikely to reduce. Recently, an internal report by the Public Health Genetics Unit has warned that the revolution in gene science and the accompanying medical remedies will be so costly that they will: *"impinge with devastating significance on clinical practice"*.

The Comprehensive Spending Review

The NHS was a major issue in the 1997 General Election campaign. In its election manifesto, the Labour Party promised to improve standards of health care and this was a factor in its resounding 1997 General Election success.

The Party had pledged that it would increase funding allocated to the NHS, but had also made the commitment that it would not raise income tax rates in the lifetime of a parliament, i.e., before the subsequent General Election. The only way that this could be achieved in the short term was to reallocate resources from other areas of government expenditure to the health service. A Comprehensive Spending Review of all government departments was begun in 1997 and, in July 1998, the Chancellor of the Exchequer announced the results of this as it affected the NHS.

It was announced that total health spending was to rise by £21,000 million over three years. This represented rises, in real terms, of 5.7% and 4.5% for the first two years, 4.7% for the third year and 4.7% for each of the two years following. In Scotland, the increase was to be £1,800 million - £300 million in the first year, £600 million in the second and £900 million in the third. This would have the effect of increasing total spending in Scotland to £4,624 million in 1998-99, £4,924 million in 1999-2000 and

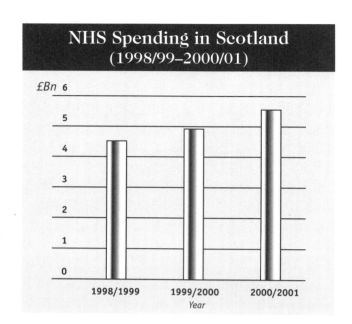

NHS Spending in Scotland
(1998/99–2000/01)

£5,534 million in 2000-01. This represents, over the period (1999-2001), an actual increase of 19.7% and of 11% in real terms.

NHS Expenditure: The Continuing Controversy

Despite the recent increases in NHS funding (£21 billion over a three year period) announced by the Government, this issue remains controversial. In 1998-99, the UK spent £46.2 billion on the NHS. At that time, total health spending, including private expenditure, accounted for 6.9% of GDP. Doctors represented by the British Medical Association (BMA) argue that if the country is to match the OECD average on health care (about 7.7% of GDP), an additional £8.4 billion would have to be spent.

In this regard, some commentators have claimed that there are 30,000 avoidable deaths annually and that this situation has received too little publicity. It is contended that such deaths are a direct result of spending approximately 0.8 per cent of GDP less than the OECD average.

In January 2000, the reported lack of beds during a flu epidemic and concerns expressed regarding the capacity of the NHS to screen and prevent the mounting incidence of cancer ensured that NHS provision and expenditure remained highly placed on the political agenda.

STUDY TOPIC 4

What have been the main challenges for the National Health Service?

"The Health service which exists today has about as much in common with its counterpart in 1948 as Concorde has with a child's kite."
(Bryan Christie, Healthbeat Scotland)

Britain's Improving Health

Life Expectancy and Disease

According to recent reports, people in Britain are becoming so healthy that the average lifespan is set to rise to 100. Dr Pat Troop, Deputy Chief Medical Officer, noted that life expectancy is rising at a rate of about two years every decade. She commented that there was no reason for this to cease over the next few decades and stated that: *"It will continue until we come to the natural life expectancy of us as an organism, which is probably around 95 to 100 years"*. A boy born now will, on average, live almost six years longer than his father, a girl just under five years longer than her mother.

Life Expectancy in Britain (Years)		
Year	Women	Men
1910	55.0	51.0
1930	63.0	58.0
1950	71.0	66.0
1970	75.0	69.0
1990	79.0	73.0
2000	79.6	74.4

This improvement has been driven by better nutrition, better housing and improvements in medical care. The major factors that have generated lengthening life-spans have been reduced infant mortality, the virtual elimination of many major diseases and measures taken to prevent illness.

Infant mortality has reduced dramatically. In 1900, 160 of every 1,000 babies died before the age of one; by 1981 this had reduced to 11 and in 1999 the figure was just 5.9 and still falling fast.

The preventive measure of vaccination has combined with better living conditions to dramatically reduce former killer diseases such as tuberculosis (TB). More than 100,000 cases of TB were recorded in Britain during 1913. In 1999, there were only 6,000 recorded cases and these resulted in just 400 deaths. Vaccination programmes have proved highly successful in eliminating a range of other infectious diseases which used to afflict many thousands of people. Whooping cough, diphtheria and tetanus have been almost completely wiped out by vaccination programmes that cover 96% of school attenders.

Improved drugs and surgical techniques are increasing survival rates for a whole range of conditions. For example, certain congenital heart conditions used to kill 98% of children who had them; now the survival rate is 30%. Childhood cancers, once completely fatal, are now cured in 60% of cases. Childhood leukaemia is now completely cured in 70% of cases.

In addition, many British people have adopted healthier lifestyles. Donald Reid, Chief Executive of the UK Public Health Association, attributes much of the improvement in health standards to healthier lifestyles. He stated: *"The bulk of the improvement is due to prevention of various kinds, and the dominant reason for that is the decline in smoking, which has fallen from one in two people in 1970 to around one in four today"*. The decline in smoking among men has meant that lung cancer has declined by a third in the past twenty years.

The development of the NHS in Britain has made an immense contribution to increasing life expectancy and as people are living longer there is greater emphasis placed on medical treatments and measures that will prolong the period during which people enjoy a healthy life free from illness and disability.

Rising Expectations and Increasing Costs

Accompanying this progress is public expectation that conditions can be treated. In 1948, 383,000 patients were treated in Scottish hospitals and 1.26 million people were treated as outpatients. In 1997, the figures were 1.3 million in-patients and a remarkable 4 million outpatients. The public today expect to be treated and to be cured. While great strides have been made in medical science and killer diseases have been eradicated, the pressures of modern life have brought to the fore new causes of illness and death. Today, in Scotland, heart disease is the biggest single cause of death and its incidence has increased since 1948. Deaths from cancer have increased by 10% between 1948 and 1995. Deaths from respiratory diseases are up from 8.1% in 1948 to 12.8% in 1995. The number of recorded suicides in Scotland between 1946-50 was less than 300. By 1996, this figure had doubled.

When the NHS was first set up, it was believed that its cost would actually decrease over the years. The reasoning behind this was that, as people were cured of their illnesses, after free treatment, their health would

Population Comparison by Age (1931 and 1991)

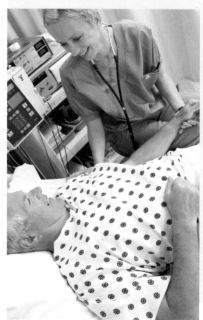

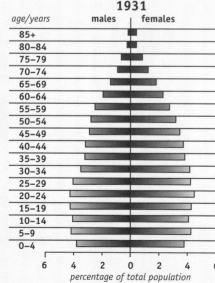

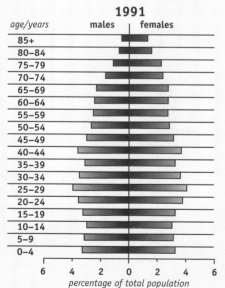

improve and, therefore, they would need to use the NHS less. With the benefit of hindsight, this may seem naive, even incredible, to us, over fifty years later.

However, the founders of the NHS were not to know the developments that were to occur and cause the opposite to happen. It is often said that the NHS is a victim of its own success. In other words, by eradicating diseases, it has caused an increase in life expectancy. With the consequential higher proportion of elderly people in the population, the demands on the NHS have grown, not diminished. People may be living longer, but elderly people tend to need more medical care than younger and what they do need tends to be more expensive. The truth of this can be confirmed simply by observing the number of nursing staff on a geriatric hospital ward compared to that on general wards. Overall, it is estimated that health care for over 75s costs seven times that for the population as a whole.

Over the years, new drugs, forms of treatment and surgery have increased the scope and cost of the NHS. It should also be noted that health care is a much more technologically sophisticated activity than before. This may be taken for granted in a technological age but it makes health care much more costly.

Medication for both physical and psychiatric illnesses and vaccinations for illnesses which were once killers, but are now almost eradicated such as polio, tuberculosis and hepatitis, have made life more worthwhile and enjoyable for patients. However, this achievement has cost the NHS sums which could not have been imagined at the time of its foundation. Surgery, such as transplantation or heart bypass, is taken for granted nowadays, but despite the fact that they are commonplace, their cost remains considerable. The use of technology in clinical areas, such as scanning or kidney dialysis, in surgery and in the administration of the NHS is necessary, but, again, not without cost.

Paying for Health

The architects of the NHS placed great faith in the third aim of the health service that it would promote good health, rather than merely treat those who had become ill. Bevan's hope was that, in the long term, the costs of the NHS to the nation would go down, as people became healthier. This has not occurred. In addition, while most people have become healthier, their expectations have risen accordingly. It is one of the achievements of the NHS that it has been able to rise to this challenge.

The questions of funding and the allocation of financial resources to the NHS have always been at the centre of the health debate. Some, such as the Scottish writer, William McIlvanney, believe that the NHS must come first in budgetary calculations: *"We shouldn't adjust our economic priorities to fit the demands of the economy. We should adjust our economic priorities to meet the demands of the National Health Service."*

Others, however, question the basic NHS principle of 'free at the point of use'. They believe that with mounting pressures on NHS finances and a growing middle class who are able and willing to pay fees but not wishing to pay increased taxes, new charges can be made. Today, health remains a political football. New Labour, in its 1997 General Election manifesto, referred back to the setting up of the NHS to attack the Conservatives: *"Labour created the NHS 50 years ago. It is under threat from the Conservatives. We want to save and modernise the NHS."*

Bevan's skills as an administrator and negotiator were tested to the limit as he encountered great opposition from the professional interest group essential to the success of the NHS. It was only seventeen days before 'Vesting Day' that the British Medical Association (BMA) gave the NHS its blessing. Ironically, today the BMA is one of the great supporters of the NHS.

In the initial post-war period, funds to build and improve health were difficult to find. This changed in the 'never had it so good' days of the 1950s and 60s when the British economy experienced its boom times. Doctors were awarded a 33% pay increase and the job of GP became one more than half of all medical students listed as their first choice. The NHS in Scotland more than doubled in size in this period and the result was more doctors and nurses, new hospitals and spectacular breakthroughs such as Britain's first kidney transplant operation, which was carried out in Edinburgh in 1960. Heart-lung machines, open heart surgery, heart and liver transplants and hip replacements all became possible through the 'technological revolution'.

By the mid 1970s, however, economic decline had re-established itself in the UK and it was clear that the NHS would have to work within much more restricted budgets. It was also becoming apparent that the population was beginning to age. More and more pensioners were increasing demands not just on health, but on social security too. An understanding of those pressures led to greater calls for efficiency and quality control.

Bevan could not have foreseen how the NHS would become a 'victim of its own success'. He had believed that, as the NHS made people healthier, they would use it on fewer occasions. This has not proved to be the case. Large numbers of people are now living beyond retirement age and are therefore not paying into the system, but instead claiming resources from it. The older people become, the more they need medical treatment and the costlier that treatment becomes. Health costs for elderly patients are seven times the cost for patients as a whole.

Paradoxically, these facts are to be celebrated as a success but impose greater costs on the NHS.

The Growing Demands for Services and Funding

Bevan resigned from the Government in 1951 when it decided to introduce charges for spectacles and dentures. In 1952, the Government introduced a flat rate charge for all dental treatment and charged one shilling (5p) for a prescription. The days of a 'free' health service lasted only four years.

Fixed prescription charges were first introduced in 1952. At that time, most drugs were available only from doctors and, therefore, through prescription. Nowadays, large pharmacy chain stores and supermarkets offer medicines for common ailments for sale to the public over the counter, often at a price less than the prescription charge. In 1998, this was £5.80, a price often barely related to the actual cost of the medicine. Some common antibiotics actually cost less than one-fifth of this, while more recent brands of medicine cost over £20. The true cost to the NHS averaged out at £9.90 per prescription. Over 80% of prescriptions are exempt from charges, including prescriptions issued for those on most social security benefits, those over retirement age, for children and for some people who suffer from chronic conditions.

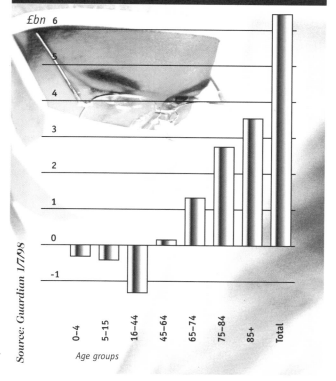

Funding Changes Needed for the NHS in 2066 to Deliver Today's Care

£bn

Age groups

0–4 5–15 16–44 45–64 65–74 75–84 85+ Total

Source: Guardian 1/7/98

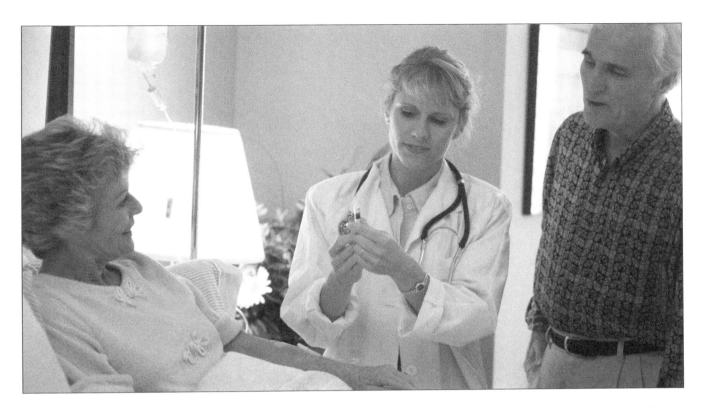

One other area where people are now having to contribute to health care, where before it was free, is long-term care. As 'Care in the Community' takes effect and elderly people and others unable to look after themselves are discharged from hospitals, they are expected to pay part of the costs of their care. This has led to a growth industry in private nursing and residential homes and has opened up opportunities for insurance companies to offer new products for those wishing to plan for their own care in the years ahead. The Labour Government set up a Royal Commission in 1997 to investigate and make recommendations on the future financing of long-term care.

The sources of NHS funding have changed little, in relation to each other, over the years. Over 95% of funding comes from public expenditure, in the form of general taxation and National Insurance contributions, including NHS contributions. The balance is from charges to patients and from miscellaneous sources, e.g., the sale of the site of a closed hospital or efficiency savings. This division is almost exactly as it was in the early 1950s, when charges first became a political issue and caused the resignation of the then Minister for Health, Aneurin Bevan.

As an illustration, charges to patients have risen from £18 million in 1952 to over £1,300 million in 1997. In relation to other sources, however, the contribution of charges to the overall NHS budget has remained almost unchanged – 3.4% in 1952 and the same figure in 1997.

However, actual and real spending on the NHS have not been so constant (real spending = actual spending adjusted for inflation). In actual spending terms (without adjustment for inflation), it rose from just over £400 million in 1950-51 to over £40,000 million in 1998-99, a staggering 100 times increase! However, when allowance is made for inflation, the budget in 1998-99 in real spending terms was just less than £2,000 million – an increase of almost five times.

A 'Funding Crisis'?

By the 1980s, some commentators suggested that a 'funding crisis' existed in the NHS. Despite government insistence that, year on year, it was spending more on the NHS than any other government, some critics stated that funding was not meeting the health needs of the country. Both claims are, in a sense, true.

Despite such dramatic rises in expenditure over the years, people have become used to expressions such as 'Funding Crisis in the NHS' being used by the press and broadcasting media in recent years. How can a public service, which has so many resources dedicated to it and that are steadily increased year on year, supplying such a range of care and held in great esteem by the people, be regarded as being in crisis? The answer lies partly in the question itself. The range and scale of the services of the NHS, as we have seen, are awesome. The NHS is regarded by the people as an institution which they expect to be funded well in order to provide these services. The Government is aware of this and continues to fund the NHS over and above the rate of inflation, trying to balance what it perceives as the legitimate demand for a properly funded NHS with the equally forceful demand for low taxation.

Nevertheless, governments of both main parties have found that the expectation of the public of what should be spent on the NHS always runs ahead of the resources that they commit. The media are ever vigilant for news stories which can justify the expression 'crisis' and report these dutifully.

The truth of the matter is that under-funding has always been an issue for the NHS, ever since its founding. Many people regard this as inevitable and some even view it as desirable. They would argue that the NHS provides services in health care which cost a great deal to provide, but are free at the point of delivery. There is, therefore, no financial disincentive for people to use the NHS, as there would be, for example, if they wanted to visit the cinema and found the price too high – and nor should there be such a disincentive, they would argue, for services which are basic needs and not simple commodities for sale in the market place. Therefore, the fact that there is no market price mechanism controlling demand for the services of the NHS means, they would argue, that the demand will never be satisfied and that funding will never be sufficient.

The NHS was established at a time of economic austerity, when Britain was recovering from the ravages of the Second World War. Its initial budget was probably not enough to meet its high ideals, given the backlog of health care caused by inadequate provision for the poor before the NHS. The founders of the NHS expected its costs to diminish rather than increase, as the population became progressively healthier. The falsehood of this expectation and the related plans for spending and their confrontation with the emerging reality of increased demands on the NHS added to its underfunding.

From the mid-1950s to the mid-1970s, there was a general increase in public expenditure, a policy which governments of both main parties shared. There was also the consensus of government intervention in the economy and high public expenditure to keep the economy growing and unemployment low. The growth in the economy and the resultant increase in tax revenues allowed more spending on the NHS, without too much increase in rates of taxation.

Although the medical success rates of the NHS and the standards of service we expect today are much higher now than then, the expectations of the people of an expanding NHS, without too much pain in the form of high income tax rates, was probably nurtured during this era.

Public Spending Cuts?

In 1976, the then Labour Government was experiencing an economic and financial crisis. It had to undertake cuts in public spending because of constraints forced on it by the International Monetary Fund. This saw the first departure from the post-war consensus of high government spending and expanding public services. When the Conservatives were elected under Margaret Thatcher in 1979, a government came to power which regarded cuts in public spending and a reduction in government activity as ideologically correct.

In contrast, the previous Labour Government had considered such action to be only a necessary temporary measure in response to strains on public finance.

Against this ideological background, one might expect the NHS to have been a prime target for the new Conservative Government, given its heavy drain on public expenditure and its status as a social institution and the one lasting achievement of a radical Labour Government. However, Mrs Thatcher stated publicly during her first term of office that the NHS was *"safe with us"*, at a time when her government was examining all areas of government activity as possible candidates for privatisation or abolition.

Indeed, an examination of spending on the NHS from 1979 to the last full year of the Conservatives' period in power reveals that, in actual terms, spending rose by 358%, an average increase of 21% per year. In real terms, taking inflation into account, the rise was 65%, an annual average of 3.8%. Therefore, the Conservatives, despite the background of the party's ideological agenda, continued to increase spending on the NHS over and above the rate of inflation. Yet, despite this increased funding, it was during this period that the term 'Funding Crisis' came to prominence.

The common perception was of 'cuts' and 'underfunding'. It is important to understand the reasons for this.

More money was spent on the NHS but much of it was absorbed by measures to reform the administration of the service. The NHS was also facing increasing demands for treatment and there was growing public consensus that 'underfunding' was a serious issue. In 1988, the Prime Minister, Margaret Thatcher, attended the Scottish Cup Final. NHS trade unions gave out 'red cards' to the fans and asked them to hold them up towards the Prime Minister. It is estimated that 40,000 fans did so. The Government could not convince the public, especially the Scottish public, that the NHS was 'safe'.

In recent times, concerns over NHS funding have been based on unfavourable comparisons with other leading European nations.

In January 2000, the Prime Minister, Mr Tony Blair, announced his intention to raise NHS spending levels to the European Union (EU) average by 2006. This was in response to mounting criticism regarding lack of progress made in reducing waiting lists for NHS treatment, a shortage of hospital beds highlighted by a flu epidemic and growing concern over the inadequacy of the NHS cancer screening and prevention programme.

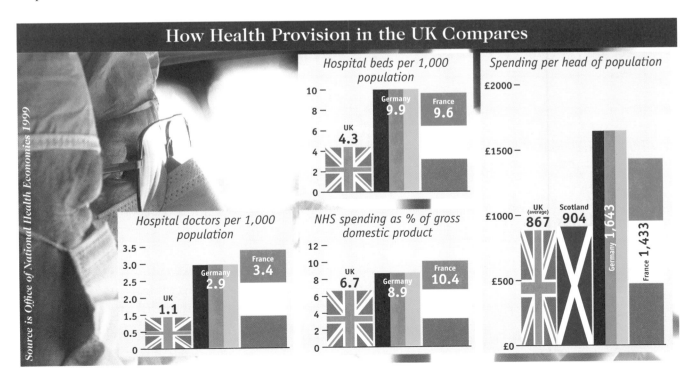

How Health Provision in the UK Compares

Source is Office of National Health Economics 1999

Hospital beds per 1,000 population
- Germany: 9.9
- France: 9.6
- UK: 4.3

Spending per head of population
- UK (average): 867
- Scotland: 904
- Germany: 1,643
- France: 1,433

Hospital doctors per 1,000 population
- France: 3.4
- Germany: 2.9
- UK: 1.1

NHS spending as % of gross domestic product
- France: 10.4
- Germany: 8.9
- UK: 6.7

Further Pressures on Funding

Changing Emphases within the NHS

NHS Budget Allocations by Percentage (1949 and 1995)	1949	1995
Hospital Services	51.3	54
Community Health Services	7.3	8.6
Pharmaceutical	7.6	11.5
GP Services	10.1	8.7
Dental	10.3	3.7
Ophthalmic Services	5.3	0.6
Other (including ambulance, mass radiography, research and development)	8.1	12.9

Source: Compendium of Health Statistics, 1997

Hospitals and the specialist services they provide have consistently taken top priority in terms of the allocation of resources within the total budget despite the move in the 1990s towards 'Care in the Community'. The growth in pharma-ceuticals reflects the range and costs of new, more effective drugs. The fall in dental and ophthalmic services can be explained by the introduction of charges for dental check-ups and, more recently, for eye-checks. As people became discouraged from having these due to cost, there was a consequential decrease in the cost of treatment and provision of articles such as spectacles and dentures by the NHS. This development also reflected culture and fashion. Contact lenses, designer spectacles and tooth-capping became items of accepted consumer expenditure.

Long-term Unemployment

Another pressure on funding is the numbers of long-term unemployed who appeared in the 1980s. The creators of the NHS believed mass unemployment to be a thing of the past. With unemployment figures of over 2 million, and sometimes 3 million, additional strain was placed on NHS resources as fewer people paid into the system. However, during the same period, demand for NHS services increased. This pressure on funding is illustrated by the rising cost of prescription charges, with those in the working population being asked to pay more and more for their treatment.

New Illnesses and Diseases

New diseases and viruses such as multiple sclerosis, ME, meningitis, HIV/AIDS and e-coli have appeared in recent years. In the midst of funding problems brought on by economic recession and changing demography, the need to fund treatment and find cures for such illnesses has represented a challenge the NHS hardly needed.

The Changing Class Structure

A further challenge came in the form of the structural changes to British society which have become noticeable since the 1980s. Before this period, the social engineering policies of post-war British governments had created a society where the majority of people, especially in Scotland, relied on the public sector. The majority of Scottish people went to state schools, lived in rented local authority housing, travelled on public transport, worked for a state-owned employer, and relied on the NHS. In the 1980s, however, as part of the Thatcher revolution, many people bought their home for the first time. For some, this was their rented local authority home. In addition, many workplaces became privatised. A large number of people bought shares for the first time and began to see themselves as 'middle class'. Despite rising unemployment, those in work saw their living standards rise. As British society became much more competitive, with clear winners and losers, those in work had new choices in life, which made them more likely to look for individual rather than collective solutions to the nation's needs.

STUDY TOPIC 5

What reforms have been made to the National Health Service by recent governments?

"If Florence Nightingale were carrying her lamp through the corridors of the NHS today, she would almost certainly be searching for the people in charge."
(Roy Griffiths, Managing Director, Sainsbury's)

Conservative NHS Reforms 1979-1997

Ideological Challenge and Change

By the 1980s, a review, not just of prescription charges, but of the entire ideology on which the NHS was founded was underway. The Conservative Government of 1979 had an ideology which was contrary to that of the 1945 Labour Government. At that time, the Conservatives, were led by Margaret Thatcher, who declared: *"there is no such thing as society"*. She championed the rights of the individual and favoured individual solutions to the nation's problems rather than collective ones. The 1980s will be remembered as the era of privatisation and the selling-off of nationalised industries to private investors. Many thought the privatisation of the NHS was inevitable.

In addressing the NHS funding problem, the Government asked Roy Griffiths, Managing Director of Sainsbury's, to conduct a fundamental review. The 'Griffiths Report', was produced in 1983 and the bulk of Griffiths' recommendations were incorporated into the 1989 Government White Paper, 'Working For Patients'. Despite the concerns of health pressure groups, such as the BMA and health service trade unions, this was to be a review that would lead to reform, not abolition of the health service.

Private finance and free market principles

Margaret Thatcher

Mirror Syndication International

were to guide the provision of services. Within this 'internal market' hospitals and GPs would now have to measure their actions on the basis of much more explicit financial calculations. For example, doctors would have to ask questions such as: *"Can I prescribe cheaper drugs than previously for patients?"* or *"Could this patient be treated more cost effectively at a different hospital?"*. In turn, hospitals would now have to think the previously unthinkable, such as sharing equipment and staff with nearby private hospitals in order to become more cost effective.

The NHS as a whole would not be privatised. However, many members of the medical profession and the public believed that these measures, described as 'creeping privatisation', would lead to the eventual privatisation of the NHS. While her Cabinet colleagues have suggested that Prime Minister Margaret Thatcher was prepared to privatise the NHS and opt for an American style private insurance system, this radical step was ultimately rejected. Similarly, other measures such as charging patients for visiting GPs were rejected on the basis that they were liable to prove unpopular with voters.

The Hotel Services

Improved efficiency was also sought in non-medical areas such as catering, laundry and cleaning. Previously, these 'hotel' services had been carried out 'in-house' by NHS staff. The Government recognised that better value for money could be had and savings made if NHS staff had to compete against private firms to provide catering, laundry and cleaning services. The result was Compulsory Competitive Tendering (CCT). It should be noted that health care, as such, had not been privatised, merely the services associated with it. The result was that firms had to compete against each other to win lucrative contracts to supply hospitals with services. Competition was on the basis of quality (who can offer the best standards of service?) and cost (who can provide the cheapest quotation for the work?). Professional hospital managers took the decision on which companies to employ.

Savings generated by this approach were used to enhance health care provision for patients.

Caring For Patients

At the end of the 1980s, some commentators reported that there was a financial crisis within the NHS. Many health authorities had put off paying suppliers until the end of the financial year. There were also strikes over pay by NHS personnel including nurses and technicians. The Conservative Government found it difficult to dissuade the electorate that it had a 'hidden agenda' to promote the private sector by starving the NHS.

The 1989 Government White Paper, 'Working For Patients', became law in April 1991. It brought about the biggest shake-up of the NHS since its creation. Once again, the British Medical Association (BMA) was to prove the biggest opponent of the Government but this time it saw its role as defending the NHS. It believed the reforms to be a 'Trojan horse' that would lead to first, creeping, then finally, complete privatisation.

It was important for the Government not only to improve the efficiency of the NHS but also to be seen to care for patients. Astutely, the White Paper, 'Working for Patients', was renamed 'Caring for Patients' when it became law. The Government believed that the new management arrangements for the NHS could only succeed if the NHS was subject to structural change. According to the Government, the managerial revolution and the performance targets of the 'Citizen's Charter' necessitated a radical review of the NHS.

Competitive Tendering

Arguments For

- increased choice to the Health Board
- higher quality of care for the patient
- savings can be redirected into patient care
- better value for money for the taxpayer
- profits for private contractors

Arguments Against

- declining standards for patients
- reduced wages, poorer working conditions for staff

What Was the Internal Market and Why Was it Controversial?

On April 1 1991, the 'internal market' was introduced as one of the key reforms of 'Caring for Patients'. The 'internal market' was not one single reform. Rather, this term was used to describe the new relationship between purchasers and providers of health care. The main purchasers of health care were health boards and new 'GP Fundholders'. The main providers were NHS Hospital Trusts and the private sector hospitals. The internal market was not privatisation as patients continued to receive care 'free at the point of use'. Indeed as Nicholas Timmins of the Financial Times pointed out: *"It is doubtful if patients noted any change at all. The battle which raged above their heads was one that involved politicians and NHS staff but left the service being delivered more or less seamlessly below"*. Timmins went on to suggest that without the 'Griffiths Report' and the 1991

reforms, the NHS would no longer exist. This argument is based on the fact that the internal market made the NHS more cost conscious and allowed it to allocate resources more efficiently in order to address issues of concern to voters such as longer waiting lists for treatment caused by increasing demand for NHS services.

Eight years later, on April 1 1999, the Blair-led Labour Government ended the 'internal market'. The Labour Government, elected in May 1997, had made a commitment to end the internal market which it believed to be 'divisive'. Instead, it sought to create a NHS where 'co-operation replaced competition'. As a result, GP Fundholding no longer exists. GPs now belong to new, 'Primary Care Groups'. NHS Trusts however remain, but they now 'work with' rather than 'compete against' each other.

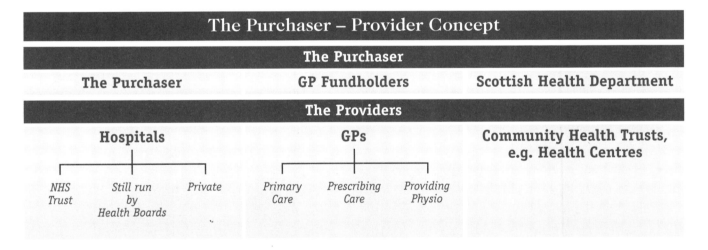

The Purchasers

Health Boards

In England and Wales, locally based health authorities are responsible for assessing the health needs of local people and making arrangements for services to be provided by NHS Trusts and other agencies. In Scotland, this role is carried out by health boards.

Health boards were first set up in 1974. They are made up of a mixture of health professionals and local people. Each regional

health board is allocated a sum of money from the Scottish Office from which it purchases health services for the local population.

As the Conservative reforms aimed to be much more focussed on primary care, that is putting GPs to the forefront of care, GPs were allocated a sum of money every year from the health board to spend in the ways they believed were most effective.

Primary Health Care and GP Fundholders

"The GP's role as gatekeeper to the hospital service is vital, ensuring appropriate referral to specialist services and making efficient use of scarce resources."

(Dr Ivan CF Wisely, Senior Partner, Brimmond Medical Group, Aberdeen)

Since the formation of the NHS, GPs have always retained a high degree of independence. Unlike salaried doctors in hospitals, GPs are considered to be self-employed practitioners. GPs have enjoyed the role of being the primary point of contact between the patient and the NHS. Although the NHS created a national structure, there has never been uniformity in GP practices. All GPs and their practices have their own individual characteristics, strengths and weaknesses.

The reforms of the Conservative years led to an enhanced role for GPs in the provision of primary health care. Under GP fundholding, GP practices became more like small businesses. This was primarily because fundholding allowed GPs to control their own budgets. It also gave doctors freedom to seek new treatments and offer new services to their patients. As long as the practice's budget could afford it, patients could be sent anywhere in the country and receive treatment from the private or voluntary sector, as well as the NHS. The key aim was to improve standards of patient care. It was believed that by increasing the choices open to GPs and patients, the 'internal market' would ensure that health care would improve. As 'money would now follow the patient', patients would be attracted to those GPs offering the best range of services. Despite the fact that the scheme was not compulsory, most GPs opted to become fundholders.

Improving Primary Health Care

There were important limitations to the new freedoms of GPs. Indicative prescribing put a ceiling on the amount of money allocated by health boards to practices for prescriptions. GPs had therefore an incentive to prescribe cheaper, generic rather than brand name drugs. GPs had also to provide certain core services to the community. For example, all GPs were required to provide a practice leaflet which explained the range of services offered and the hours the practice was open as well as providing information about the GPs working in the practice. In addition, GP practices were required to make 24 hours a day arrangements for patient care and GPs had to live within reasonable travelling distance of the practice.

To enhance the GPs' primary care role as 'gatekeepers' to the system, doctors were given a more proactive role within the community. For example, practices were encouraged to attract new patients by providing high quality services. The Government set 'realistic but challenging' targets for child immunisation and cervical smears. In relation to cervical smears, the doctors had to see 80% of women in the practice aged 20-64 over a five year period.

Alongside these strict guidelines, GPs were given powers to expand their practices and provide new services. An October 1996 survey by *Which* magazine found that a wide range of services were being offered by the new fundholding GPs. These included 'Well Person Clinics' as well as clinics for smoking, family planning, healthy eating and stress and weight management.

The Providers - NHS Trusts, the Private and Voluntary Sectors

In order to become a provider in the internal market, health organisations became NHS Trusts. Essentially, they were independent organisations with their own managements competing against each other. The first NHS Trusts came into being in 1991. By 1996, all health care was provided by NHS Trusts.

There are very few large hospitals in Scotland that do not now have trust status. The old directly managed unit hospitals (DMUs) disappeared altogether as part of New Labour's reforms. NHS Trusts are not private hospitals. Treatment for the patient goes on much as before. No fee is charged for treatment, it continues to be 'free at the point of use'.

Each NHS Trust has its own board of directors composed of a chairperson, five executive members (trust managers) and five non-executive members. Before the Scottish Parliament, the chairperson and non-executive members were appointed by the Secretary of State for Scotland but now they will be appointed by the First Minister of the Scottish Parliament. The executive members are appointed by non-executive members.

What does Trust Status mean for a Hospital?

Trust status allows a hospital to become much more independent in the decisions it takes about the care it provides. Between 1992 and 1999, NHS Trusts were financed by a grant from the Scottish Office. They are now financed by a grant from the Scottish Parliament. Trusts must provide services which are essential to the local community.

Some hospitals specialise in heart or respiratory care, others in, for example, maternity care. A hospital can only provide services that someone is willing to purchase. The amount of grant the trust hospital receives is determined by the amount of operations it carries out. Just like a private firm, a 'successful' hospital attracts the business of purchasers. It must be emphasised that trusts remain part of the NHS and continue to provide NHS treatment and services.

From the patient's point of view, little had been privatised as a result of the 'internal market'. The 'internal market' remained true to the core principle of the NHS expressed as 'care which is free at the point of use'. No money changed hands between the patient and the provider. The market was internal to the system created by purchasers and the providers. In theory, the patient (or customer) is put at the centre, in the belief that better service will result if 'the money follows the patient'. Doctors who established themselves as fundholders competed for patients. As their practices increased in size, they received additional funding from the local health board. Hospitals, too, if they established themselves as NHS Trusts, competed for patients. These patients were referred by doctors who

believed that the hospitals selected were able to offer higher standards of care and service, along with shorter waiting periods for treatment.

Professional Administrators

Previously, senior members of staff were appointed from within. These people were essentially health service employees. As such, they had a commitment to the values of the NHS but did not necessarily have a business approach to health care. They were replaced by professionally qualified managers, often recruited from the private sector, with business degrees such as Master of Business Administration (MBA). Some of those appointed had little knowledge of delivering a health care service.

This was sometimes seen as an advantage as they could bring in tried and tested business methods which 'inside' administrators may have been wary of introducing.

What these new managers possessed was an approach which put 'customer' (i.e. patient) care first and established clear performance targets for hospitals to reach. Treatment would only take place when it was considered to be both clinically and financially practical.

The Patients' Charter

The Patient Has the Right to:

- treatment regardless of income, sex, race or disability
- accept or refuse treatment
- refuse to be examined or treated in front of students
- refuse to be invovled in research trials
- a twelve month maximum wait for in-patient treatment
- seek a review of the clinical decisions about an illness
- a specific, named nurse dealing with the patient
- to be told of whether care will be in a single or mixed ward before entering hospital

Mrs Thatcher was succeeded as Prime Minister by John Major in 1990. A feature of the Major Government was its emphasis on efficient management of industries in the public sector. A key step was the introduction of a series of 'Citizens' Charters'. These emphasised the rights of the consumer in terms of public service provision. The Government required that there should be recognised quality standards that all public sector workers should strive to meet. If these were not met, the public had the right to hold the service accountable and expect compensation.

The 'Patients' Charter' was one of the best known of the 'Citizens' Charters'. It began with a restatement of the basic aim of the NHS: *"to provide care on the basis of clinical need, not ability to pay, lifestyle or any other factor"*.

The rights contained within the 'Patients' Charter' were not legal rights but statements of intent by the Government. The Labour Government, elected in 1997, has accepted the principle of charters in raising standards and charters remain a familiar aspect of NHS provision.

The Access to Health Records Act 1990 also gives patients the right to see information held about them which has been produced by health professionals. This applies to information recorded after 1 November, 1991. The Data Protection Act 1984 already allowed access to health files held on computer.

Conservative NHS Reforms 1979-1997: Competition, Improved Management and Increased Efficiency?

Like any major reform, there are some who believe in its merits and others who believe it to have been a step in the wrong direction. Supporters of the Conservative reforms claim that they were necessary and that restructuring had to take place if the NHS was to survive. Speaking at the 1998 Conservative Party conference, Anne Widdecombe MP claimed that the Conservatives had saved the NHS: *"Only the introduction of business methods saved the NHS from bankruptcy."*

Anne Widdecombe MP with Conservative leader William Hague

There are few consumers who would buy from a business that had long queues for service, unattractive products, expensive prices, and rude, unhelpful staff. Most consumers would take their custom elsewhere. It is therefore competition between businesses to attract custom that drives down prices, encourages innovation and improves standards, all of which benefit the consumer. It was claimed that such competition would act to improve the NHS and that it should be run more like a commercial enterprise (albeit with no money changing hands between patient and provider).

According to this view, the competitive element of the 'internal market', i.e, more popular hospitals and successful GP Fundholders attracting greater funding, would create healthy competition which benefited patients. As all partners in health care had an incentive to treat patients with respect, the best standard of treatment would be on offer.

Anne Widdecombe, Shadow Home Secretary, claimed that the key to improved management of hospital budgets was to put hospitals in charge of their own financial affairs. A central idea underpinning the creation of NHS trust hospitals was the belief that professional executives could make better decisions than distant bureaucrats in health boards. It was local managers who had best insight to issues such as the hours doctors and nurses needed to work, the type of services most popular with patients and possible savings. It was argued that they were in a better position to determine opening times and those health needs of the local community that could be addressed by preventive measures. Increasing independence would result in trust hospitals becoming more efficient.

A further way of improving efficiency, it was claimed, was to have hospitals specialise in a particular type of care. Instead of a general hospital trying to offer all types of care as a 'jack of all trades', hospitals should specialise in areas of treatment that they are best able to provide. The recent decision to concentrate heart operations for Scottish children in Glasgow was evidence of this thinking.

A Two Tier Service?

Many opposed the reforms on the ideological basis that business principles could not readily be imported to the NHS. According to critics of the internal market, as private companies exist to make profits for owners and shareholders they operate on a different level from the NHS which is a service to the country.

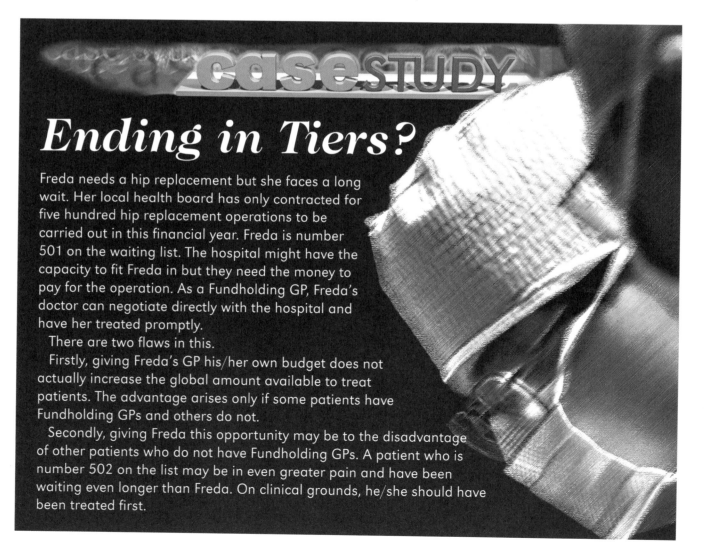

case STUDY

Ending in Tiers?

Freda needs a hip replacement but she faces a long wait. Her local health board has only contracted for five hundred hip replacement operations to be carried out in this financial year. Freda is number 501 on the waiting list. The hospital might have the capacity to fit Freda in but they need the money to pay for the operation. As a Fundholding GP, Freda's doctor can negotiate directly with the hospital and have her treated promptly.

There are two flaws in this.

Firstly, giving Freda's GP his/her own budget does not actually increase the global amount available to treat patients. The advantage arises only if some patients have Fundholding GPs and others do not.

Secondly, giving Freda this opportunity may be to the disadvantage of other patients who do not have Fundholding GPs. A patient who is number 502 on the list may be in even greater pain and have been waiting even longer than Freda. On clinical grounds, he/she should have been treated first.

Those opposed to the reforms believed the 'internal market' meant the end of the NHS ideal of a national service aiming to treat all patients equally, regardless of their social or economic circumstances. They claimed that a 'two tier' NHS was developing. According to this view, far from modernising the NHS, the 'internal market' was a step back to the days before the NHS, when those with higher levels of income could obtain health care denied to others.

Critics of Conservative NHS reforms pointed out that if a patient, through no fault of their own, could not be registered with a Fundholding GP, he or she may not have the same access to treatment as another patient whose GP is a Fundholder. In many rural areas of Scotland, there may be only one GP available. In such a situation, the concept of competition and 'money following the patient' would not apply. In addition, patients of GP Fundholders, could 'jump the queue' for treatment as a Fundholding GP could send a patient to any hospital in Scotland selecting one where treatment is more advanced or where waiting times are shorter. For example, a GP Fundholder in Falkirk could offer a hospital appointment in Inverness to his patient, if this was the best possible solution. A non-fundholding patient may have to wait longer. It was also argued that because a GP Fundholder had money to spend and NHS Trusts had to sell their services, the latter might give priority to a fundholder over a non-fundholder.

A *Which* survey that found that although the new services offered by GP Fundholders were impressive, there were marked geographical variations in the availability of these services. While GP services have never been of uniform nature, critics of the reforms claimed that the NHS could no longer claim to be a truly national service.

Two-tier Dentistry?

Another example is dental care. A *Which* survey conducted in 1998 found that only 53% of dentists were willing to take on new NHS patients. While many dentists continue to work within the NHS and accept NHS patients, some are attracted by the opportunity to make much more money working outside of the NHS in private practice. As many as one in four dental patients in the UK have now 'gone private'. Private patients can pay a regular amount, sometimes as low as £20 per month (by direct debit), to ensure that all their dental needs, from fillings to crowns can be met. Patients can enjoy the comfort and ease of private treatment, which at times compares favourably with NHS dental care. A private dentist located in an affluent part of town may be able to afford to see fewer patients, therefore spending more time with each individual. Waiting times may be shorter and facilities more comfortable. Such private care is within the reach of many families in the UK today since it is likely to be cheaper than, for example, a monthly subscription to digital television. It does, however, further erode one of the basic principles of the NHS, that care be 'comprehensive and free of charge'. Private patients can 'jump the queues' they may encounter in NHS practices.

However, for some people, the option of paying for a private dentist may not exist. Dental practices are becoming concentrated in more affluent areas, leaving some poorer council estates with fewer dental facilities. This 'Inverse Care Law' was highlighted by the 1979 'Black Report' on health inequalities.

It may be argued that dental care facilities are being denied to some of the people who need them most.

Looking for Savings

A further concern was expressed by some in the medical profession that doctors should only make medical decisions, not financial ones. Their talents lie in being doctors, not accountants. Through constantly looking for budget savings, a Fundholding GP may have a financial incentive to prescribe the cheapest treatment to a patient rather than the best treatment. This may destroy the trust that should exist between patient and doctor. It could also lead to GPs not taking on 'expensive' patients, e.g., the old or the long-term ill, the very people who most need health care.

Economies of Scale

Critics of NHS Trusts point to the loss of 'economies of scale' from the old health authority system. In the past, savings could be made by health authorities buying capital equipment in bulk such as medical supplies. These would be allocated to NHS hospitals and savings passed on for patient care. As Trust Hospitals worked independently and, in theory, against each other, these savings were lost. Hospitals could buy the same equipment and services, benefiting no one. It was claimed that NHS staff such as doctors stopped sharing good practices with their colleagues in other hospitals. Their contract with their 'own hospital' encouraged them to work in isolation to boost the performance of their individual hospital rather than advance health care for all NHS patients.

Reference was also made to the alleged inefficiencies of the 'internal market' with vast amounts of money being squandered by hospitals needlessly competing with one another. Some argued that budgets spent on advertising, consultancy, managers and solicitors could have been better spent on direct patient care.

The End of the Internal Market

Opinion was divided among NHS professionals and pressure groups on the success of the 'internal market'. The new Labour Government, elected in 1997, acknowledged that many of the reforms made by the Conservatives should stay. It approved of the 'Patients' Charter'. The Labour Government supported the accountability that the 'Patients' Charter' brought to the health service and the good practices it encouraged among doctors. The Government also approved of allowing GPs a greater role in decision making within primary health care. Similarly, the Labour Government believed that the creation of trust hospitals allowed local managers to make better decisions on operational health matters. The key objection was to the development of a two-tier system of health care within the National Health Service.

Private v Public - an Outdated Notion?

Concerns over the development of a two-tier system of health care were addressed by means of New Labour's ideology of the 'Third Way'. This is the belief that the issue of whether ownership and provision of a service is within the public sector is to some extent irrelevant. According to the Labour Government, what is most important is the quality of service to the consumer. This 'Third Way' is neither the socialist way of 'Old Labour', which favoured state ownership and provision, nor is it the capitalist way of the Conservative Party, which has traditionally favoured private ownership and provision. The 'Third Way', it is argued, is based on the reality that the divisions between state, private and voluntary sectors are not as clear cut as may be imagined and that all three groups can complement one another.

The emergence of private financing of NHS hospitals is one indication that the dividing line between state and private health is blurring. Another is the growing use of private pay beds within NHS hospitals and the sharing of capital equipment between NHS hospitals

and local private hospitals. It has been known for some time that some NHS doctors and nurses have 'moonlighted' in the private sector. This means that they have a work contract with the NHS but secretly work in the private sector for extra cash. The 'Third Way' would end the secretive 'poaching' of staff and allow more harmonious relations between the different providers of health care.

The Private Finance Initiative

What is likely to emerge in future is a more explicit link between the public and private sectors. The increased use of the Private Finance Initiative (PFI), introduced by John Major's Government in 1992, makes this inevitable. One example is the building of the new Edinburgh Royal Infirmary. This new NHS hospital, to be completed in 2003, is being built by private contractors and will be leased to the Government which will pay a rent to the private owners to use it. The hospital will continue to accept NHS patients free of charge but will also accept private patients and employ private medical consultants for 'profitable' operations. The profits will then be reinvested for public provision.

The Voluntary Sector

Some hospitals in the UK, most famously Great Ormond Street Hospital for Children in London, exist as providers of health care on a voluntary basis. Other voluntary hospitals exist for those suffering from specific illnesses such as mental illness, physical or learning difficulties, HIV/AIDS or misuse of alcohol or drugs. The voluntary sector will also play a part in health care by raising funds for a specific hospital.

The Sick Kids Friends Foundation is a charity formed to provide 'additional' resources for the Edinburgh Sick Kids NHS Trust. Examples of help it has provided are:

- In 1996, the purchase of a Retrieval System which ensures that, when a child is being brought in to the hospital from a long distance, treatment can begin on the journey. This cost £47,000.

- In 1997, £97,000 was made available to help provide a new digital EEG system, to more accurately diagnose conditions such as epilepsy and sleep disorders.

Money was raised through sponsored runs, a hospital shop, fund-raising by local celebrities, e.g., from local Radio Forth and the Scottish Claymores, and private donations.

Some people are opposed to the voluntary sector making such a large contribution to health care. They believe that such fund-raising is unjust and a throwback to the pre-NHS era of charity hospitals which provided for those unable to pay. Charity hospital provision is precisely what the NHS was set up to eradicate. Others take a less ideological and more pragmatic view. They claim that the source of funding takes second place to the immediate meeting of need.

The Private Sector

Fears over NHS Standards

Public fears that the NHS was being slowly privatised grew with stories such as that of David Barber, a 'hole in the heart baby' from Birmingham. He had his operation cancelled five times in six weeks due to a lack of money. Faced with this level of service, the option of private medical insurance (PMI) became increasingly attractive. The numbers of people taking out PMI grew more in the 1980s than in any other period. During the recession of the early part of the decade, there was a public loss of faith in the NHS' ability to provide prompt and satisfactory treatment. Despite the economic boom of 1984-1988, the NHS did not appear to improve.

With fears over standards of NHS care and increasing economic prosperity, some of those who could afford it decided to 'opt out' of the NHS and instead pay for private treatment. This growth in private medical insurance had the effect that it enlarged the private health market and enticed some medical staff to leave the NHS. However, the growth in PMI meant that a significant proportion of the population was in fact paying twice, private insurance premiums and national insurance contributions, for health care.

During the General Election campaign of 1992, the Labour Party attempted to capitalise on public fears expressed by the public over possible NHS privatisation. Its controversial party political broadcast, 'Jennifer's Ear', focussed on two young girls who required ear surgery. Jennifer's parents could not afford private medical insurance, and while Jennifer waited in pain for the impoverished NHS to treat her, the other more affluent girl received immediate treatment from a private hospital. The broadcast attempted to portray Conservative health policy as leading to both privatisation of the NHS and the existence of a two tier health system.

Pick of the Medical Policies*				
Company	Single Person aged 29	Married couple aged 45+ 2 children under 15	Married couple aged 60+	Special features
Bupa	£61.12	£222.38	£243.32	Premiums fixed for five years
PPP Healthcare	£30.83	£106.92	£118.74	Only pays for treatment if NHS waiting list is more than 12 weeks
Norwich Union	£33.99	£125.84	£176.42	Offers private treatment or £250 a night cashback if NHS bed is chosen
Prime Health	£32.55	£106.56	£153.78	Standard policy
PHC	£30.97	£101.75	£131.41	Does not exclude pre-existing conditions if switching from another insurer
Secure Health	£29.84	£94	£119.51	Standard Policy
Royal & Sun Alliance	£34.86	£95.67	£152.49	Standard Policy

*Monthly premium for full in-patient treatment at selected hospitals

Private Medical Insurance

Private patients, if they have the means or the insurance cover, can be treated privately. Health can be insured in much the same way as a car. Those with good health records and with good health prospects pay less than someone in worse health since members of the latter group are more likely to make 'claims' on their health insurance. In the immediate period after the setting up of the NHS, less than 2% of people in the UK were covered by private medical insurance (PMI). Its growth began in the 1960s. Due to government enforced limits on pay rises, many companies began offering PMI as a way of rewarding staff.

Demand for PMI grew enormously in the Thatcher years. In 1989, Mrs Thatcher allowed tax relief on PMI for those aged over 65 (this was abolished by the Labour Government in 1997). In 1999, approximately, six million people, 11% of the UK population, relied on private medical insurance (PMI) in preference to the National Health Service. Those people were concentrated in the richest 25% of the population. PMI is provided by high profile companies such as BUPA and AXA, who advertise heavily to sell their health care to people anxious about the quality and promptness of NHS care. BUPA, for example, sponsor the popular Edinburgh 10 km road race and AXA have sponsored the English FA Cup. As BUPA themselves put it: *"the NHS can't always cope with the huge demand for 'non-urgent' operations - so you or a member of your family could be faced with a long, uncomfortable wait"*. BUPA advertises its insurance schemes from as *"little as 50p a day"* and offers a range of benefits to individuals.

Private Health Care - For and Against

The debate over PMI has become less polarised in recent years. This is because more people now use the private sector and a new generation of adults looks upon individual choice as a fundamental human right.

Consumer Sovereignty

Supporters of PMI believe in the individualist philosophy. They argue that an individual should enjoy the freedom to spend his or her money on better health care if that is what they want and that the Government should not be able to prevent this. After all, it is argued, PMI can cost less per day than a packet of cigarettes. It is claimed by some that PMI actually benefits the NHS as it removes people from NHS waiting lists.

Those who subscribe to the individualist philosophy see health as a choice. They feel that many illnesses in today's society are the result of poor lifestyle choices, e.g., smoking and excessive consumption of alcohol. They believe that the taxpayer should not have to foot the bill for this type of overindulgence. People should be encouraged to meet their own health care needs. Also, some purchasers of PMI do not wish to have to spend on health care twice. Why, they argue, should taxes be paid for the NHS when some individuals already pay for their own health care?

This concept of 'consumer sovereignty' is illustrated by some of the benefits of private health care: immediate treatment, pleasant surroundings, privacy and the doctor or surgeon of your choosing.

Some people simply do not feel they can trust the NHS with their health. They contend that the quality of health care available in the NHS is inadequate. Since political parties do not have the political will to raise taxes to enable major increased spending on the NHS, this group has chosen the private option.

This view is a consequence of the transformation of the country's social class structure fostered by the 1980s' 'Thatcher revolution'. As Chancellor Gordon Brown, in January 1999 stated: *"We are a middle class nation now"*. Similarly, the former dictator of Chile, Augusto Pinochet, asserted: *"Once most people in the country have their own house and a car, they will forget about socialism"*.

Limited Access

While many former 'working class' people have improved their living standards in recent years, many others, e.g., the long-term unemployed or those on a low income living in poorer council estates, have seen their life

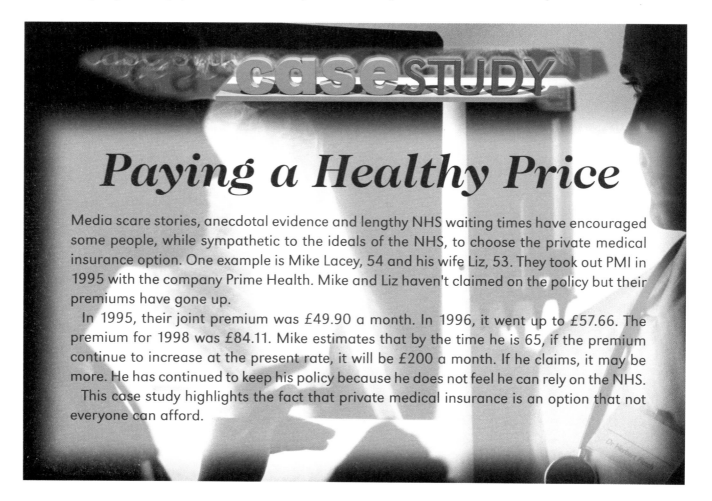

case STUDY

Paying a Healthy Price

Media scare stories, anecdotal evidence and lengthy NHS waiting times have encouraged some people, while sympathetic to the ideals of the NHS, to choose the private medical insurance option. One example is Mike Lacey, 54 and his wife Liz, 53. They took out PMI in 1995 with the company Prime Health. Mike and Liz haven't claimed on the policy but their premiums have gone up.

In 1995, their joint premium was £49.90 a month. In 1996, it went up to £57.66. The premium for 1998 was £84.11. Mike estimates that by the time he is 65, if the premium continue to increase at the present rate, it will be £200 a month. If he claims, it may be more. He has continued to keep his policy because he does not feel he can rely on the NHS.

This case study highlights the fact that private medical insurance is an option that not everyone can afford.

chances deteriorate. The Joseph Rowntree Foundation estimates that as many as 1 in 3 children are brought up in poverty. Private medical insurance is low down their list of priorities.

Justice for All

Opponents of PMI believe that health care is a fundamental right. PMI, it is asserted, weakens the NHS and is fundamentally immoral. Health is not a consumer good, like holidays or cars, and money should not be able to buy better health care. These adversaries maintain that financial crises can be solved only if there is the political will. An NHS which depends on an annual scramble for funds of grant applications, fun runs, coffee mornings and car boot sales does not suggest that society is taking the provision of health care for all of its citizens too seriously.

They also claim that the very existence of PMI leads to the best doctors and nurses being lured to private practice where they can earn more in less stressful conditions. It is claimed that, if standards in the NHS were as good as they could be, there would be no reason for doctors, nurses and patients to join the private sector. Another criticism is that most doctors and nurses have been educated and trained by the British taxpayer, therefore, PMI is cashing in on public investment.

The American Experience

Some commentators claim that if PMI continues to grow, British health care will resemble that existent in the USA where the public sector treats mainly the poor and the terminally ill, whom the private sector shun.

They also point to the fact that US hospitals have high administration costs. In 1999, bureaucracy accounted for fully 26% of the cost of providing patient care in an average US hospital. In contrast, administration charges ranged from 2% to 6% in NHS hospitals.

Those opposed to the growth of PMI conclude that as long as there is PMI for the 'haves' in society, a group most likely to be politically powerful, there is less political pressure on governments to raise general taxation and to fund the NHS adequately. Consequently, it is feared that the Government may rely more on charitable donations to maintain hospitals. This would conflict with the original NHS ideal of providing health care for all.

An Alternative to PMI

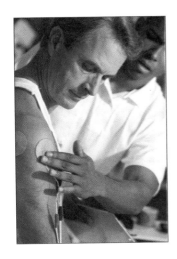

A growing number of people are opting to pay for private treatment as and when they need it rather than pay money every month for private medical insurance that they may not use. It is estimated that a family of four would pay more than £2,500 a year for PMI. Over a number of years they would have to be treated for several major illnesses before insurance worked out cheaper.

The Cost of Common Operations	
Operation	**Amount**
Heart bypass	£9,500 - £12,500
Knee replacement	£5,700 - £8,400
Hip replacement	£5,000 - £7,800
Hysterectomy	£2,300 - £4,300
Varicose veins	£1,300 - £1,425
Hernia	£1,350 - £1,700
Cataracts	£1,950 - £2,600
Face lift	£1,500 - £7,000

Source: Nuffield Hospitals/Bupa

The NHS and New Labour Reforms

> *"Previous reforms sought to promote efficiency by competition, pitting practice against practice, hospital against hospital, and trust against trust. The result was a complex, fragmentary and inefficient management structure that divided resources and multiplied managerial costs. The new structure is simple and efficient, reflecting the demise of the internal market. Fundholding will go."*
>
> **(Dr Colin Currie, Medical Director of Edinburgh Healthcare NHS Trust)**

Health Care Reforms of New Labour

- The internal market abolished
- GP Fundholding abolished
- Larger community-based GP cooperatives introduced
- NHS Trusts have remained but in larger units
- Responsibility for health care rests with the Scottish Parliament
- Private companies to build and own new hospitals through the Private Finance Initiative (PFI)

The Labour Party has always seen itself as the only political party capable of maintaining the original ideals of the NHS. While 'New Labour' has changed a great deal of 'Old Labour' ideology and policy, New Labour has committed itself to providing free health care. The Labour Party's 1997 Election manifesto promised to: *"restore the NHS as a public service working co-operatively for patients, not a commercial business driven by competition"*.

Maintaining Bevan's Vision

The Labour Government sets itself the task of maintaining the vision of Bevan's original NHS aims but with 'modern' methods. This has meant abolishing the Conservative Party's 'internal market' and GP Fundholding, replacing these reforms with larger community-based GP cooperatives. NHS Trusts have remained in place, but have joined together into larger units. Responsibility for health care in Scotland now rests with the Scottish Parliament. 'New Labour' is also willing to allow private companies, through the Private Finance Initiative (PFI) the opportunity to build and own new hospitals.

Designed to Care

In December 1997, the UK Government launched a White Paper, 'The New NHS: Modern, Dependable'. In Scotland, the reform was entitled: 'Designed to Care'. Scottish Secretary, Donald Dewar, emphasised: *"This will be an NHS designed to cooperate, not compete, designed to deliver, not delay, and above all designed to care"*. In May 1999, responsibility for the NHS in Scotland passed from the Scottish Office to the new Scottish Parliament.

The Labour Government, since 1997 has made specific pledges, which it sees, as realisable. It has made a financial commitment to health care: "This government will back the NHS in Scotland by raising spending on health in real terms every year." It has also promised to:

Labour's NHS Pledges

- Cut Waiting lists by 100,000.
- Make £100m of savings.
- Establish NHS Direct, a 24 hour telephone advice line, which will be staffed by qualified nurses.
- Set up the National Institute for Clinical Excellence to ensure consistently high standards of care are provided equally across the country.
- Establish NHSnet to electronically link doctors surgeries.
- By the year 2002, patients should know the date of their hospital appointment when they leave the surgery.
- Introduce one-stop clinics to provide tests, results and diagnoses on the same day.
- Cut down the numbers of NHS Trusts.
- Create two different types of Trust; Acute Hospital Trusts and Primary Care Groups. (Creation of Primary Care Groups will end GP Fundholding.)
- Introduce a public health strategy that will tackle the underlying causes of ill health.

Most crucially, the reforms mean the end of the internal market and GP Fundholding. The emphasis now is much more on how the providers of health care will cooperate with each other.

The Health Boards

Scotland has fifteen regional health boards. As before, their role will be to identify the health care needs of the people living in their area. They will draw up three year Health Improvement Programmes, in consultation with local NHS Trusts and the new Primary Care Groups. Health boards will allocate funds to these Primary Care Groups and hold them to account. Health boards will take a more active health promotional health care role, and perform a 'watchdog' service in health standards similar to the role played by the Advertising Standards Authority.

NHS Trusts

Hospitals have been allowed to retain trust status and take day to day decisions themselves. The Government, however, is determined to change the emphasis of trust management, so that trusts co-operate with each other rather than compete. This, the Government believes, will result in health care being "patient driven rather than market driven" and delivered in a spirit of co-operation and partnership. Trusts will be separated into Acute Hospital Trusts and Primary Care Trusts and it is estimated that the number of NHS hospital trusts in existence in Scotland will decline from the present 47 to around 28, thereby saving £110m in management costs.

Acute Hospital Trusts

Acute Hospital Trusts will be responsible for specific acute hospital services (for example, a Trust may specialise in heart disease) within the geographical boundaries of a specific Health Board. Each Health Board should have one Acute Hospital Trust, but large Health Boards such as Glasgow and Lothians may have two. They will be obliged, by law, to cooperate with other NHS Trusts and Care Groups and will contribute to the overall Health Improvement Programme.

Primary Care Trusts

Primary Care Trusts were introduced in April 1999 to replace GP Fundholders. These comprise of local GP practices, community hospitals and mental health services. They have the power to become free standing Primary Care NHS Trusts. Within each Primary Care Trust are Local Health Care Cooperatives. These work within geographical areas that have specific local health needs. Local Health Care Cooperatives have the power to hold budgets for primary and community services. All are electronically linked. Cooperatives appoint their own staff, but within the guidelines set by the Primary Care Trust. While each Local Health Cooperative is managed separately, it is part of the overall Primary Care Trust. The Primary Care Trust allocates cash but allows each Local Health Cooperative to have its own budget.

Primary Care Trusts, along with Health Boards and Acute NHS Trusts, will set up the Health Improvement Programmes (HImPs) to set targets for improved patient care and use performance indicators to measure if these targets have been met.

Primary Care Trusts

- consist of GP Practices, Community Hospitals and Mental Health Services
- Local Health Care Cooperatives deal with the needs of specific geographical areas
- hold budgets for primary and community services
- electronically linked
- appoint staff
- managed separately

The Role of GPs and Primary Health Care Teams

The Government is placing increasing emphasis on primary care. This is often referred to as the 'front line' of the NHS. The new primary health care teams include GPs, health visitors, district nurses, midwives and sometimes social workers. Together they provide a service which plays an important part in promoting health and keeping people well in addition to treating them when they are sick. Working within Local Health Cooperatives, they help to plan the full range

of services needed by local people and help decide how those services should be provided.

The new system builds on the greater powers given to GPs in recent years. The majority of GPs work in group practices. GPs are the first point of contact most people have with the NHS. Most people who visit their doctor do not need clinical treatment but rather advice or counselling on a healthier lifestyle. Primary health care teams provide an opportunity for other health professionals to work with GPs to improve health in a local area. The services provided through GP practices may also include speech therapy or family planning.

In 1997, the Labour Government launched the 'Investing in Dentistry Scheme'. This provides financial incentives for dentists to remain in the NHS and improve dental care in deprived areas of the country.

Primary Health Care Teams

- GPs
- Health visitors
- District nurses
- Midwives
- Social workers
- Speech therapists

Contrasting Views

The new system has been welcomed by some GPs. Dr Ronald MacVicar, an Inverness GP, has argued that the changes make sense and build on the good practices that have been going on at present in the Inverness area. Since July 1997, all twelve practices in the Inverness and Culloden area, involving 43 GPs and almost 60,000 patients, have effectively been working as a cooperative, while each still retained its independence. Dr MacVicar stated: *"GP Fundholding was a very cumbersome system. It allowed you to buy from a specific list, it encouraged you to play shoppies between different hospitals, but we were in an area where there was only one hospital, Raigmore. All it did was give you a bit of a voice in the system. What we wanted to do was use that kind of empowerment of general practice, but in a much less bureaucratic way. Not with one practice, but with them all. We would share the administration and it would give us a much bigger patient base".*

However, not all GPs share this perspective. They point to the decision making capacity afforded by GP Fundholding arrangements and express concerns that the new system may not allow them to provide such high quality care. Dr Gary MacFarlane, a GP in Kilsyth, noted: *"There were thousands of patients throughout Scotland benefiting from services brought in through fundholding. Over the last three or four years as a GP, I have been able to practise the best medicine I have ever been able to provide because I have been able to make these decisions for myself. I don't think health boards and trusts really want to move towards a primary care-led service".*

Dr MacFarlane referred to the speedy appointments that he was able to arrange for angina and cardiac ultrasound patients. He is worried too that other specialised practices, such as eye clinics in Lothians, may have to go. He also expressed cash concerns about the new system and is concerned that, rather than cutting bureaucracy, the new reforms would simply create another layer of red tape and prevent GPs from doing their jobs.

The BMA perspective, in Scotland, was provided by Dr Brian Potter, Scottish Secretary of the BMA. He gave the changes a broad welcome and commented: *"GP Fundholding, with its potential for two-tier treatment, was a bad thing and any attempt to address that has to be applauded. It will take a long time to resolve the problems of the NHS but this is a very good start. However, we will be watching the Government closely. It is easy to say that they have the commitment, but those words will have to be matched by deeds"*.

Nevertheless, some observers remain critical of the steps that the Labour Government has taken and claim that, rather than abolishing GP Fundholding, the new primary care groups, in effect, make every GP a fundholder. In this regard, a great deal will depend on the relationship that develops between GPs and the Primary Care Trusts. Some GPs have already expressed concern that the Primary Care Trusts may be able to exert considerable financial pressure on GP practices. Among the questions asked by GPs are: *"What happens when GPs overspend?"*, and *"Do the managers running the Primary Care Trusts have the right to decide what happens to GP practices if money has to be saved?"*. The answers to questions such as these will determine the extent to which GPs are free to act in the best interests of their patients.

Improving Standards?

'Designed to Care' also emphasises higher levels of quality and efficiency within the NHS. There will be nationally recognised standards, published and available to the public, which state the minimum standards of care patients should expect. This is called the 'National Service Framework'. In addition, a 'National Institute for Clinical Excellence' will be set up. This will be comprised of academics, doctors, patients and economists who will disseminate good practice on a national basis.

The 'Commission for Health Improvement' will have powers to inspect the workings of hospitals to ensure that high standards are maintained and verify that the 'National Framework' is being implemented.

The Government does not see health care as an isolated part of its social policy. It believes that the existing social class inequalities are not accidental or merely the result of 'bad' choices made by weak individuals. 'Health Action Zones' have been set up in deprived areas. These exist to deliver better, preventive health care measures to people who in the past have suffered ill health through living in impoverished areas.

The Private Finance Initiative

"We have launched the biggest ever hospital building programme in Scotland's history, with almost £500 million of investment pledged to provide 8 new hospitals and facilities including Edinburgh Royal Infirmary, Benbecula and Hairmyres. It is only through developing the partnership between the public and private sectors from the Private Finance Initiative that these investments are achievable in this time scale. They are good value for money."

(Scottish New Labour Handbook, 1999)

The Private Finance Initiative (PFI) was introduced by the Conservative Government in 1992. It means that new public sector buildings or redevelopment of existing buildings in schools or hospitals can be funded and owned by private business. In the NHS setting, this usually means that a new hospital, for example, the new Edinburgh Royal Infirmary will be built by a number of private companies (called a 'consortium'). Edinburgh Royal Infirmary NHS Trust will then pay the consortium a monthly sum for the use of the facilities.

For a new hospital project to be given planning permission from the local health board and the Scottish Parliament, a PFI deal must be affordable in rental costs and cost less than a publicly funded scheme. Lease agreements between the NHS Trust and the private consortium normally last twenty five years.

PFI is a classic example of a 'Third Way' solution to public ownership of the economy. 'New Labour' ministers have famously been told to 'think the unthinkable' by Prime Minister, Tony Blair, in addressing social issues. 'Old Labour' would have supported state ownership of hospitals as a matter of principle and opposed private ownership on the same basis. The so-called 'Third Way' approach of Tony Blair is based on the view that the issue of ownership, in this sense, is largely irrelevant. Advocates of PFI and other such initiatives contend that the question *"Does it work?"* should be asked instead.

In 1999, there were thirty four NHS PFI projects underway in Scotland. Some examples are:

Health Board/NHS Trust	Project Description	Capital Value (£m)
Ayrshire/Arran Health Board (Saltcoats)	90 Elderly care beds	2.5
Dundee Teaching Hospitals NHS Trust	Re-equipping of X-ray department	4.3
Grampian Health Board (Spynie Hospital)	25 beds for mentally ill	1.1
Yorkhill NHS Trust	Replacement of 2 heating boilers	0.7
Lanarkshire Acute NHS Trust	Replacement of Hairmyres Hospital	25

The new Hairmyres Hospital under construction

Throughout Britain, there are those who are in favour of PFI and those who oppose it. The most obvious benefit is to the taxpayer, at least in the short term. No extra public spending is required to finance new hospital developments. These buildings can be built now rather being shelved until funds become available. This allows the Trust concerned to concentrate on spending its funds on health care, leaving the issue of construction and maintenance to the consortium.

Those who oppose PFI believe that it will lead to the increasing privatisation of the NHS. They disagree, politically, with private companies making a profit from the NHS. Economically, they believe that PFI represents bad value for money for the taxpayer as the long-term costs of PFI are unknown, and ultimately the facilities will never belong to the NHS. NHS Trusts will always be paying rent to the consortium.

Things Can Only Get Better?

The Labour Party, while in opposition, opposed all of the Conservatives' legislation on the NHS and criticised government funding as inadequate. Arguably, it was the soundbite of *"things can only get better"*, especially in relation to health care, that helped 'New Labour' to win the support needed to secure victory in the 1997 General Election.

The 'internal market' has been abolished but opinion among the medical profession is divided over the likely success of the reforms. Some GPs liked the independence fund-holding delivered and the choice and speed it brought to patient care. Others believed that it meant a two-tier service, rationing and inferior care, rather than providing the best care for patients. The Government has sought to allow hospital trusts to maintain their independence over financial and clinical decision making, while ending competition between NHS hospitals and GPs.

Ultimately, however, to deliver the kind of NHS provision that voters expect, more money will have to be found. This could come from higher taxes, charging for services, and/or changing entitlement to prescriptions.

Higher Taxes

Much of the cost of the NHS is paid for through general taxation. Total UK expenditure on the NHS in 1997-98 was £44,719 million. This represented 5.7% of GDP and a cost per head to the population of £758. To substantially improve standards of patient care, the Government would almost certainly have to spend more money. This could come from raising taxes. However, 'New Labour' is very wary about this. Many of its new voters, especially in the Midlands and South of

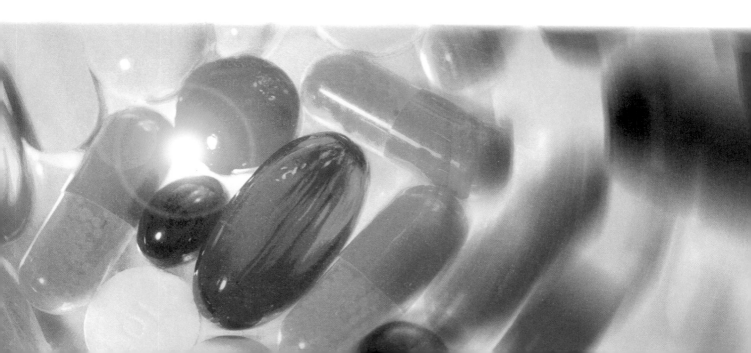

England, have private medical plans and may not wish to vote for a party seen as 'throwing money at a problem'. Although the new Scottish Parliament has the power to vary Income Tax by up to 3% and could increase tax, it has promised not to do so in the short term. The Scottish Parliament has responsibility for health care and health care spending in Scotland. In 1998, this cost £3.6 billion, one third of the new Scottish Parliament's entire budget.

Charging for Services

Another option is to implement charges for those who use NHS services. It is estimated that a £10 fee for visiting a doctor would bring in £3.3 billion. Supporters of this option point to the example of Sweden which has always charged for GP appointments. However, it has fewer health inequalities than the UK. According to 'New Labour' thinker, John Willman, in his influential book 'A Better State of Health', there is an increasing willingness by some groups of people to pay for health if it means a higher standard of service.

He cites the example of the 70,000 people each year who are willing to pay £37.50 for holiday vaccinations and the total of £500 million per year which is spent on alternative therapies such as homeopathy and osteopathy. In the field of primary health care, organisations such as Parkside Private Clinic in Glasgow have been set up. Parkside offers the services of a 24 hour home visit by a GP for £40. This is around the same price as a call out charge for a plumber.

Changes to Prescriptions

Restricting access to free prescriptions has also been considered by the Government. In 1997-98, it was estimated that 85% of medical prescriptions were supplied free of charge. Those entitled to free prescriptions include children under the age of 16, those young people under 19 in full time education, pregnant women and new mothers, war pensioners and people with certain medical

conditions or on low incomes. In 1997-98, the cost of those prescriptions came to £4400 million. Another estimated £1000 million is lost through fraudulent prescription claims. The Government has embarked on measures to tackle this.

Public Resistance to Charges

In recent times, many commentators have argued that the challenges faced by the NHS are so great that only a fundamental rethink of the issue of funding will save the day. According to this view, there will have to be greatly increased rationing of health care and charging for treatment to cope with the combined pressures of increasing public demand and expectations.

This already bleak situation is being exacerbated by the fact that new treatments, particularly in relation to the prevention, treatment and cure of cancer, will place tremendous pressure on the NHS.

Gordon McVie, Director General of the Cancer Research Campaign commented, in October 1999, that the health service would not be able to cope with what he referred to as: *"an explosion in new ways of preventing and treating cancer"* which a growing understanding of genetics is making possible. The issue of cancer is particularly sensitive in Britain where death rates are already significantly higher than in Europe and the United States.

Professor McVie, in condem-ning what he viewed as a disgraceful record in treating cancer patients, noted that there were many deficiencies in UK provision. He cited the fact that new drugs such as 'Taxol' which can extend the lives of young women with ovarian cancer were not being funded and noted that radiotherapy machines were 20 years out of date.

Also, he made reference to the fact the the 'Calman-Hine' review of cancer care which recommended that patients should see cancer specialists in centres of excellence instead of general consultants at local hospitals was not being implemented.

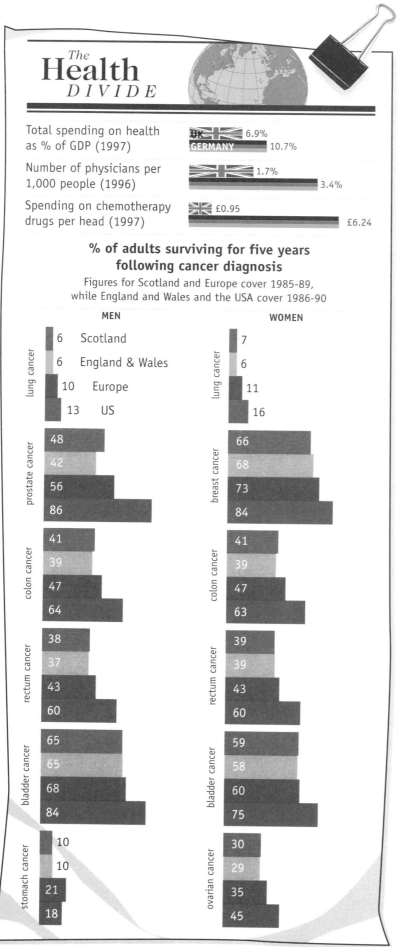

The Health DIVIDE

Total spending on health as % of GDP (1997)	UK	6.9%
	GERMANY	10.7%
Number of physicians per 1,000 people (1996)	UK	1.7%
		3.4%
Spending on chemotherapy drugs per head (1997)	UK	£0.95
		£6.24

% of adults surviving for five years following cancer diagnosis

Figures for Scotland and Europe cover 1985-89, while England and Wales and the USA cover 1986-90

MEN

lung cancer
- 6 Scotland
- 6 England & Wales
- 10 Europe
- 13 US

prostate cancer
- 48
- 42
- 56
- 86

colon cancer
- 41
- 39
- 47
- 64

rectum cancer
- 38
- 37
- 43
- 60

bladder cancer
- 65
- 65
- 68
- 84

stomach cancer
- 10
- 10
- 21
- 18

WOMEN

lung cancer
- 7
- 6
- 11
- 16

breast cancer
- 66
- 68
- 73
- 84

colon cancer
- 41
- 39
- 47
- 63

rectum cancer
- 39
- 39
- 43
- 60

bladder cancer
- 59
- 58
- 60
- 75

ovarian cancer
- 30
- 29
- 35
- 45

Source: OECD, WHO, Royal College of Radiologists, Institute of Economic Affairs

In addition, a new generation of drugs has improved the chances of survival from many types of cancer. 'Taxol' for ovarian cancer, 'Taxotere' for breast cancer and 'Irinotecan' for bowel cancer have all proved effective but at between £3,000 and £5,000 per course of treatment, some health authorities have refused to prescribe on grounds of cost. Limited NHS budgets mean that they will be available only for those who can afford to pay.

Despite increasing awareness on the part of the public that the NHS rations the latest and most effective treatments, there is clear resistance to paying for health care. A 1999 review conducted by the Nuffield Trust revealed that only 14% of those surveyed would be willing to pay to visit their GP and a meagre 6% to receive hospital treatment.

This finding was backed by an opinion survey of 2,000 people carried out by the Social Market Foundation. Asked how they would like to pay for the NHS if they had to do so, only 19% opted for higher income tax. However, 44% said they would prefer a special tax earmarked for the NHS alone.

Such findings clearly reflect the dilemma faced by the current Labour Government and all recent British governments. Medical advances are helping with preventive health care and improved lifestyles to increase life expectancy. Previously incurable ailments can now be treated and sometimes cured. As a result of these developments, public demand for and expectation of NHS provision is increasing all of the time. However, the general public remain resistant to increased taxation and charging to finance NHS provision.

A Universal Service or Free at the Point of Use

The political rows over these issues highlight both the economic reality of matching resources with need and the social changes in British society. While there are groups of people with the disposable income to afford to pay for such as physiotherapy or private home visits by a doctor, for other less well off groups this is an impossibility.

Most health experts acknowledge that it will be some years before we can fully assess the success of 'New Labour's' reforms. However, political rows over PFI and charges are likely. The Blair Government has to try to please both its 'new' supporters who have the finance to pay privately for a range of medical services and do not approve of tax increases, and its more 'traditional' supporters, many of whom live in Scotland, who demand increased state provision. Some of these supporters can remember the days before the NHS. According to John Willman, the dilemma is that the Government may have to choose which one of the NHS ideals it values most: *"preserving one of the NHS's fundamental values, a universal service, can only be achieved by sacrificing another – free at the point of use."*

Labour and the NHS: A Summary of Developments

The Labour Government's plans for the NHS were outlined in its White Paper – 'The New NHS' – published in 1997. Among the developments introduced by the Government were the following:

NHS Direct

This is a confidential NHS service designed to offer advice and information about health problems and available support. NHS Direct is intended to provide 24 hour access to free advice from a trained health professional, usually a qualified and experienced nurse, for the cost of a local call. Should the situation prove to be an emergency, the call will be passed immediately by NHS Direct staff to the emergency services.

NHS Direct now covers 65% of England and it fielded 10,600 calls on Christmas Day 1999, 14,800 calls on New Year's Day 2000, compared with a daily average of 5,000 calls in the autumn of 1999. In a new development announced in January 2000, doctors will be offered the option of having all their out-of-hours calls dealt with by NHS Direct and the nurses on duty will decide on whether a home visit is necessary.

NHS Direct

NHS Direct is a newly introduced 24-hour telephone advice and information line staffed by nurses. I has been piloted during 1999 and will be extended to most of the UK during 2000. During the January 2000 influenza epidemic, it received more calls than it could handle.

Primary Care Groups

Known in Scotland as Primary Care Teams, these new groups which were introduced in April 1999, are intended to put GPs, nurses and health professionals in the driving seat in shaping local services. According to the Government, they will change the way that GPs work together in local communities so that they can improve services for patients, increase the quality of care and tackle health inequalities more effectively. They have the power to advise on a range of hospital services for the patients in their community.

NHSnet

This is the approach taken by the NHS to the opportunities provided by the 'information superhighway'. It is intended that the Internet will help to streamline NHS administration by supporting the electronic transfer of clinical information including health records. By the year 2002, it is intended that electronic transfer of records will exist throughout the United Kingdom.

Our Healthier Nation

This document, a Green Paper published in 1998, expressed the Government's aims to improve the health of the population, with particular reference to the worst off in society, in order to narrow the health gap. It sets targets to reduce deaths from heart disease and stroke, cancer and suicide and to cut the number of accidents.

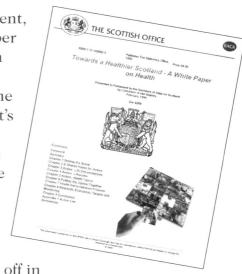

In Scotland, the relevant document was the Government's 1998 Green Paper, 'Working Together for a Healthier Scotland' which led to the 1999 White Paper detailing the Government's intentions entitled, 'Towards a Healthier Scotland - A White Paper on Health'.

Headline Targets for Scotland	
Coronary Heart Disease	Reduce by 50% between 1995 and 2010: ie from 143 to 72 deaths per 100,000 population.
Cancer	Reduce by 20% between 1995 and 2010: ie from 188 to 150 deaths per 100,000 population.
Smoking	Reduce smoking among young people from 14% to 12% between 1995 and 2005 and to 11% by 2010.
	Reduce the proportion of women who smoke during pregnancy from 29% to 23% between 1995 and 2005 and to 20% by 2010.
Alcohol Misuse	Reduce the incidence of adults exceeding weekly limits:
	from 33% to 31% for men between 1995 and 2005 and to 29% by 2010.
	from 13% to 12% for women between 1995 and 2005 and to 11% by 2010.
Teenage Pregnancy	Reduce by 20% between 1995 and 2010.
Dental Health	60% of 5 year olds to have no experience of dental disease by 2010.

National Institute for Clinical Excellence (NICE)

This new body is intended to assist the Government in coping with medical advances and the need to be cost effective by promoting clinical and cost effectiveness of NHS services. It advises on best practice in the use of existing treatment options and advises on the use of new treatments and technology.

A related aspect of the work of NICE is to remove unacceptable regional variations in health care which were aggravated by the operation of the 'internal market'.

According to the Government, NICE will identify those new developments that will most improve patient care and spread their use quickly across the NHS.

Commission for Health Improvement (CHI)

The Commission's role is to ensure that standards are being met. Local health care organisations in the NHS will be reviewed every 3 or 4 years by the 'Commission for Health Improvement'.

National Service Frameworks (NSFs)

This body is intended to reduce unacceptable variations in standards of care and treatment. NSFs for coronary heart disease and mental health were published in 1999 and further NSFs will be published in the near future for the care and treatment of the elderly and diabetes sufferers.

Conclusion

From the above developments, the Government's approach to the development of the NHS is clear. It aims to reduce pressure on the health service by improving front line, primary health care and thereby enhance the capacity of the NHS to respond quickly to patients' needs. While taking this step it is also ensuring value for money by increasing

the accountability of those who work within the NHS. In addition, the introduction of the 'National Institute for Clinical Excellence' (NICE) is an attempt to rationalise and phase the introduction of medical advances and new treatments within the NHS.

Implementing Labour's NHS Reforms: An Update

NHS Funding

In January 2000, the Prime Minister, Mr Tony Blair, gave a pledge to raise NHS funding by 5% a year in real terms to put Britain on a par with the European Union (EU) average of health spending by 2006. The Prime Minister was reacting to concerns expressed by leading medical experts, including Lord Winston, a Labour peer, over the shortage of hospital beds during the flu epidemic of the winter of 1999/2000, Britain's comparatively poor record in preventing and treating major diseases such as cancer and a seeming lack of progress in reducing waiting lists for NHS treatment.

Since Mr Blair's statement, there has been some controversy as to whether it represented an aspiration or a firm commitment. Nevertheless, a number of commentators have welcomed a projected increase in real spending amounting to 25% of the NHS's total budget.

Many take the view that voters will judge Labour's commitment to the NHS in terms of the efforts that it makes to reach that target.

Geographical Inequalities

A further dimension that the Government has had to deal with has been the issue of geographical inequalities. In this regard, criticism has been particularly acute due to inequalities in the provision of cancer care. Studies have shown that wide variations exist in the provision of cancer care across the UK. Nigella Lawson, writing in the Guardian newspaper commented: *"Rather than having a National Health Service it is as if we have dozens of independent health services, all operating under different rules and using different criteria. In some parts of the country, you'll be booked into a specialist cancer hospital which will spend thousands on chemotherapy drugs even though the success rates of some drugs for cancer are minuscule; in others, you'll be told that your time is up even though there are plenty of well proven cures which might well succeed."*

Geographical inequality is also evidenced by imbalances in funding and the cost of treatment. Official figures show that the NHS spends about £1,000 per year on each Scot. In contrast, only £800 is spent on each person living in England.

This funding imbalance manifests itself in differences in NHS provision. In Scotland, there are 51 consultants per 100,000 population against 39 per 100,000 in England. Furthermore, Scotland has 75 GPs per 100,000 population against 56 per 100,000 in England. The contrast in the provision of nurses is also significant, 808 nurses per 100,000 population in Scotland compared to England's 620.

However, even within England there are significant differences in funding. The Isle of Wight, which has the most elderly population in England and the lowest household income, will receive a rise in NHS funding of 3.6% after inflation in 2000-2001. This contrasts with a national average of 4.2% and the amount allocated to the London authority of Kensington, Chelsea and Westminster for the same period (2000-2001) is fully 5.9% after inflation.

Disturbingly, hospital operations can cost up to 20 times more in one part of England than another according to government statistics. That figure highlights the gulf between the minimum and maximum costs across the country for the same operation. For example, a lung transplant can cost as little as £2,488 but as much as £31,430 with an average of £19,292. A hip operation ranges

from £354 to £7,784 between hospitals. The average cost of a hip operation is £3,755.

Accountability

As the Labour Government has sought to make NHS staff more accountable, it has met with some opposition. The Government's new health watchdog, the 'Commission for Health Improvement' (CHI) has the task of inspecting every hospital and GP practice in the country every four years. The Commission will send teams of doctors, nurses and other health professionals into every hospital and Primary Care Trust to review standards of care and ensure that patient complaints are properly dealt with. It will also ensure that doctors are using the latest technologies and effective medicines.

The Commission can order a hospital or Primary Care Trust to implement changes and, if there is insufficient improvement, it can sack a trust board and report doctors to their professional bodies. In addition, doctors are to undergo annual assessment in order to ensure that they remain capable of working competently.

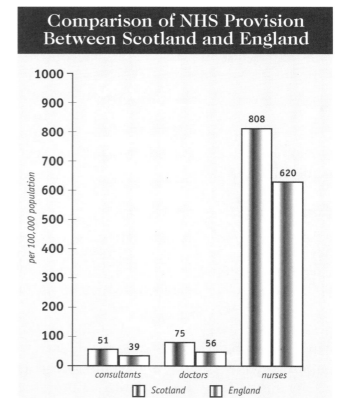

Comparison of NHS Provision Between Scotland and England

Inequalities in Health

STUDY TOPIC 1

To what extent do hereditary and environmental factors influence health?

Introduction

When the National Health Service was set up in 1948, one of its founding principles was to provide a service of equal quality for everyone. The NHS aimed to reduce the inequalities in health that existed throughout the United Kingdom. Before 1948, the different regions of the country had wide variations in standards of health care provision. Generally, cities had better facilities than rural areas and wealthier areas provided better health care than poorer areas. In aiming to reduce these inequalities, the new National Health Service set itself a very difficult task.

Fifty years after the establishment of the National Health Service, it is clear that there still remain great inequalities in health within the United Kingdom. Despite great improvements in medical knowledge and technology and the creation of a universal health care system across the United Kingdom, these inequalities in health are still obvious. This situation exists due to the difficulties experienced in attempting to eliminate social inequality.

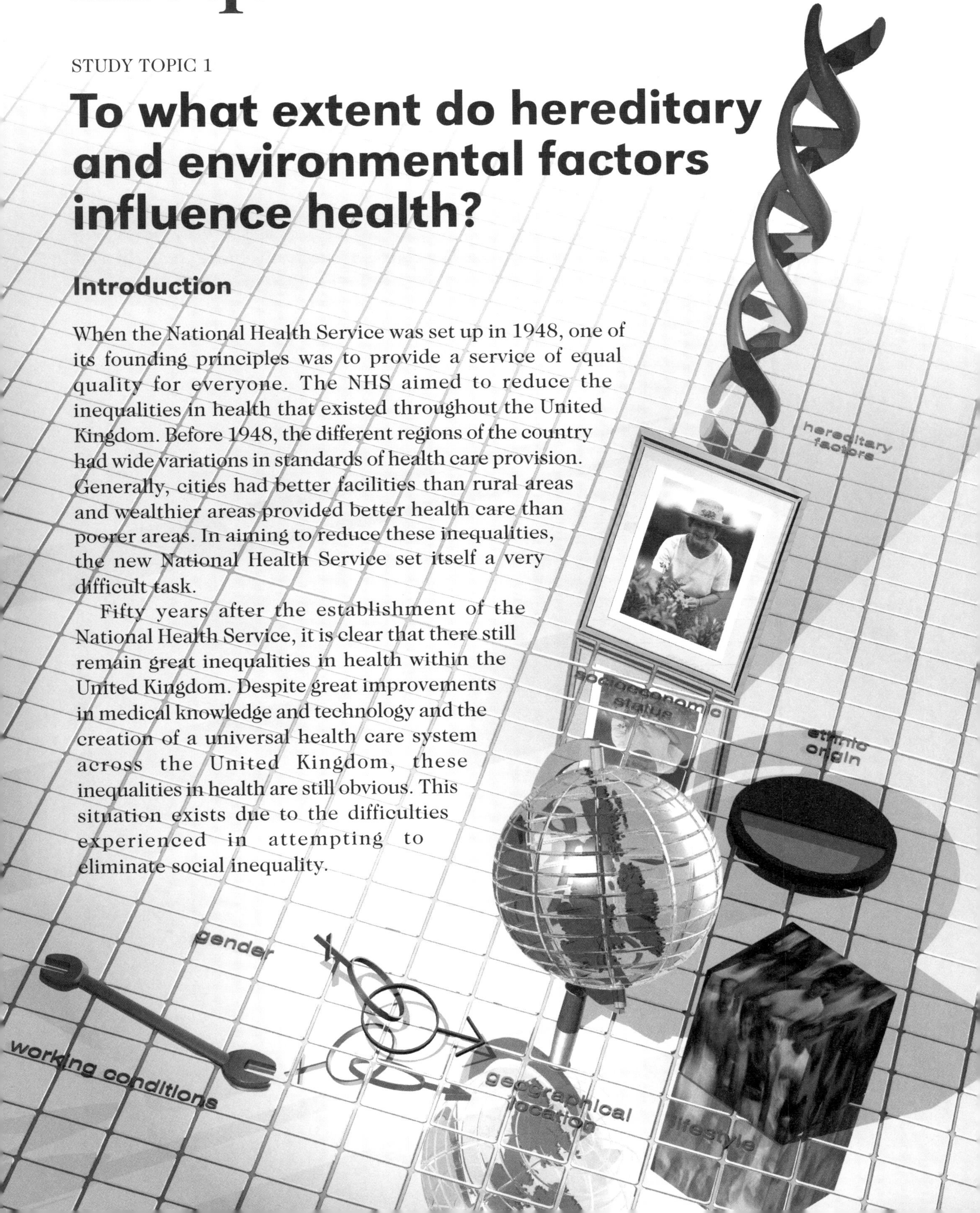

hereditary factors

socioeconomic status

ethnic origin

gender

working conditions

geographical location

lifestyle

Health Inequalities in Scotland

Local Inequality

Glasgow provides one example of sharp inequality within a small geographical area. Two newborn babies living just a mile apart on the north side of Glasgow, one in Bearsden and one in Drumchapel, have very different life chances due to the contrasting nature of their respective environments. Bearsden is a much more prosperous area and people living there enjoy considerable social and economic advantages. Accordingly, people living in Bearsden are generally much healthier than those in nearby Drumchapel as the statistics opposite show.

On Average:

- One baby will live ten years less than the other.
- One is two and a half times more likely to die before the age of 65 than the other.
- One is twice as likely to die before it is a month old.
- One is three times more likely to die of heart disease or bronchitis.
- One is three times more likely to die of breast cancer.
- One is twice as likely to die of lung cancer.
- One is four times more likely than the other to suffer psychiatric disorder.

National Inequality

Health inequalities like this often exist at a local level. However, the national picture is equally disturbing. Dr James Inglis, Director of Health Information at the Health Education Board for Scotland (HEBS), is appalled at the rapidly growing divide across Scotland. He said that similar differences could be found within every major town and city, but also between cities. For example, people in Edinburgh live four years longer than those in Glasgow. Dr Inglis put this down to a combination of poorer housing and diet, higher smoking rates and poverty.

Causes of Death and Numbers of Psychiatric Admissions across Selected Areas in Scotland				
Area	Heart Disease (deaths per 1000)	Malignant Tumours (deaths per 1000)	Strokes (deaths (per 1000)	Psychiatric Admissions (per 100,000 people)
Borders	4.1	3.3	1.6	512
Grampian	3.3	2.6	1.4	532
Greater Glasgow	4.0	3.5	1.6	638
Highlands	3.7	2.7	1.6	538
Lothian (incl. Edinburgh)	3.4	2.9	1.5	589
Tayside	4.3	3.2	1.6	526
Scotland (average)	3.8	3.0	1.5	570

International Inequality

Scotland is often portrayed as a country with serious health problems. Compared to other parts of Europe and the USA, Scotland has very high rates of cancer, heart disease and other serious health problems. In addition, cancer survival rates are poor.

Causes of Health Inequalities

There is no simple explanation for the health inequalities that are noted to exist within Scotland and when Scotland is compared with other countries. Various elements, including hereditary factors, lifestyle, working conditions, socio-economic status (social class), gender, ethnic origin and geographical location, interact to produce the health patterns of an area.

Factors Which Influence Health
Hereditary Factors
Lifestyle
Working Conditions
Socio-economic Status (Social Class)
Gender
Ethnic Origin
Geographical Location

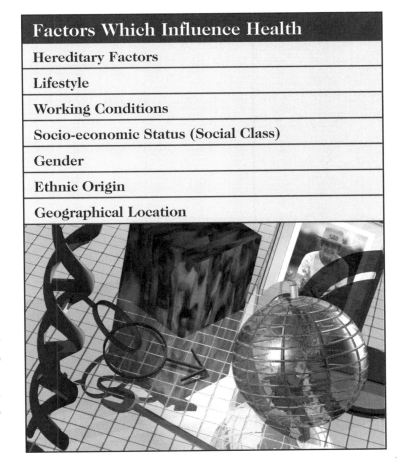

Factors Influencing Health

Hereditary Factors and Health

Every person is born with their own pattern of genes, passed on from their parents, that determine their sex, size, shape, colouring and other features. Once a person has been born, there is nothing that they can do about the genetic fingerprint which they have inherited. Research into genetic factors and recent developments in genetic engineering are highly controversial areas of scientific and medical research.

Researchers have found that there are specific genes which make a person more or less likely to develop particular diseases or medical problems. Downs Syndrome and Haemophilia are entirely genetic in nature in the sense that all cases can be explained by particular genetic defects. Scientists recently identified a gene which they think suppresses appetite. Some people lack this gene and this could contribute to obesity. In other illnesses such as heart disease, cancer and Alzheimer's Disease, evidence suggests that there is a genetic link but not in all cases. The likelihood of any one person developing these and other illnesses may be greater in that they have a particular gene pattern. However, it is important to emphasise that they can also develop the illnesses without any genetic link.

It's All in the Genes / Family Fortunes

It is well-known how some families will have a history of particular health problems. The likelihood of having a heart attack or stroke is higher if previous generations of the family have shown a tendency to suffer from these conditions. Just as you may take after one or both of your parents in appearance then you may inherit their health characteristics as well.

Various answers have been suggested to deal with the effect of genes on health. The crudest solution is for people to avoid having children if they possess particular gene patterns. However, not every child will inherit every gene from its parents. During pregnancy, a foetus can be tested for abnormalities and, depending on the outcome, the decision can be taken to terminate the pregnancy. However, this opens up serious moral issues. What is normal? How seriously affected must an unborn child be? Can any of these justify termination of the pregnancy?

In the late 20th century, it became possible to have 'test tube babies'. The techniques of 'in-vitro fertilisation' allow carefully selected genes to be brought together from the sperm and ova of the donors, thereby producing a process of genetic selection. Again this raises serious moral issues. For example, what are the risks that donors may knowingly have genes that could lead to a higher incidence of abnormality or deformity?

There are two particular illnesses, Haemophilia and Duchenne Muscular Dystrophy, where women carry the gene but only male children inherit the disease. In this case, it might seem easy to terminate any pregnancy as soon as the foetus is identified as male. However, this sort of decision would have serious ethical and social implications for society.

Genetic Manipulation and Dolly the Sheep

In the past, it was not possible for people to make decisions based on genetic factors. They simply did not have the information. Indeed, they did not know whether a child would be male or female until the moment it was born. Nowadays, with advances in medical technology, people can have detailed knowledge of hereditary factors and they can make decisions based on them.

The potential for this will increase in future years. Eugenics is the name given to the scientific study of means of improving the human race through genetic manipulation. If cloning of mammals such as sheep was possible in 1997 then who knows what might be possible by 2007. Dolly, the cloned sheep, made her appearance in 1997 yet by 1999 scientists were concerned that she was showing signs of premature ageing, opening up further controversy on this issue.

On a positive note, people can make important health decisions and choices based on knowledge of their own genetic fingerprint. If they possess a gene which makes them more likely to suffer heart attacks then they will be able to make positive decisions about lifestyle and diet to reduce their likelihood of being affected or to make the effects less severe.

Lifestyle and Health

There is a direct link between lifestyle and health. Doctors often ask their patients a series of questions that relate to their lifestyle but are known to have a direct impact on health. Examples of such questions are as follows: *"How many cigarettes do you smoke each day? How many units of alcohol do you consume each week? Do you take drugs? How often do you exercise each week? How many portions of fresh fruit and vegetables do you eat each day?"*.

The answers to these questions reveal much about a person's lifestyle. Lifestyle has a considerable effect on health. Consideration of two extremes reinforces this point. At one extreme is the 40 cigarettes a day, spirits-drinking, overweight male who considers a 50 yards stroll to the nearest public house a long walk. His diet is unhealthy with little, if any, fresh fruit and vegetables and many fatty, processed foods. At the opposite end of the spectrum is the non-smoker who enjoys an occasional glass of red wine. Jogging and working-out in a gymnasium are his favourite pastimes and he follows a careful diet plan based on fresh fruit and salads to ensure he gets the correct balance of nutrients.

Lifestyles like these can affect a person's health. There are no certainties regarding the impact of lifestyle on health. However, there are probabilities and the probability is that the second person will be healthier and live longer than the first. Nevertheless, it remains within the bounds of possibility that the first person may live to a fine old age, while the second person may drop dead of a heart attack at any time.

Unemployment

The circumstances of people's lives may have a profound effect on their health. Unemployment has affected several hundred thousand people in Scotland throughout the 1990s. It brings with it feelings of despair and low self-esteem. Unemployed people are less likely to be able to afford a balanced diet and they may seek consolation from tobacco, alcohol or drugs, each of which may have serious consequences for their physical and mental health. Poor housing conditions, often associated with poverty, also lead to health problems. In 1996, 25% of Scotland's houses were judged to suffer from condensation or dampness, conditions which can aggravate respiratory (breathing) illnesses. Lead water pipes can contaminate water and lead to restricted intellectual development in children.

The Environment

The environment also has an effect on health. It is clear that pollutants can damage health but the condition of the environment is of wider significance. A pleasant environment with open spaces and recreational areas encourages people to walk and enjoy fresh air whereas an environment of dereliction, heavy traffic and industry encourages people to stay in their homes. Areas that suffer from multiple deprivation, due to a combination of various social and economic factors, represent a serious health risk to the people who live there. Regeneration of such areas to provide better housing, more jobs and better facilities is an expensive task which can be undertaken by government, the private sector, the voluntary sector or most likely a combination of all three.

The Labour Government, elected in 1997, placed particular emphasis on dealing with the problem of 'social exclusion'. During the 1980s and 1990s, an 'underclass' developed in Britain. This included people who had never held down a secure job, had few qualifications and little training, low incomes and poor self-esteem, often living in the most run-down and undesirable ghetto housing estates. Health standards amongst those who are socially excluded are likely to be poor. Some specific health problems such as HIV/AIDS may even contribute to the exclusion of individuals. In attempting to tackle the problem of 'social exclusion' and the poor health standards which accompany it, the Government acknowledged the need to make health services accessible, affordable and user-friendly. Accompanied by wider knowledge of health-related issues, improved living conditions, better employment opportunities and consequently the potential to earn higher incomes, the Government hoped that health standards could be improved amongst this disadvantaged group.

Smoking

The effects of smoking kill approximately 2000 people per week in Britain. Tobacco smoke, and the tars contained within it, is implicated in a number of cancers, from the mouth and tongue all the way through the trachea, bronchus and into the lungs. Other more remote parts of the body may also be affected including the gullet, pancreas, bladder and, in women, the cervix. In addition, the carbon monoxide in tobacco smoke enters the blood stream, reducing the amount of oxygen to the brain leading to blockages in blood vessels. The most vulnerable areas for this are the heart, the brain and the outer limbs. The result is that Scotland, with its high smoking rates, has one of the highest rates in the world of coronary heart disease, strokes, amputation of the limbs through peripheral vascular disease and lung cancer.

'Passive smoking' has also attracted considerable attention. People who spend a lot of time in an atmosphere where there is cigarette smoke will absorb some of the harmful side-effects, even if they do not smoke themselves. Unborn children are particularly susceptible to the effects of 'passive smoking'. Recent studies have shown that smoking by mothers during pregnancy increases the likelihood of 'cot death' seven-fold. The children of parents who smoke are also at increased risk of asthma and other respiratory problems, as well as lung cancer.

Consequently, smoking is now banned in many public places. Workplaces usually have designated smoking areas where people can smoke during their breaks but they cannot smoke in work areas or the main recreation areas. Smoking is forbidden on most buses and trains and in many places of entertainment. Restaurants usually have smoking and non-smoking areas. This has come about because of increased public concern about the dangers of 'passive smoking'. Although there is strong medical evidence to link smoking to a wide range of health problems, it would be difficult for the Government to ban smoking completely. This would be regarded as an infringement of people's civil liberties and would immediately criminalise a huge number of people. However, successive governments have been criticised for not doing more to discourage smoking. Some commentators suggest that higher taxes and restrictions on the advertising of tobacco products and the sponsoring of sports and arts events by leading tobacco companies would help reduce smoking further.

Cigarette advertising is not allowed on television and the content of magazine and billboard adverts is strictly controlled. A ban on tobacco advertising might make little difference to the number of people who smoke. Although smoking amongst mature adults has fallen over the last thirty years, the number of young people who smoke has remained constant at around 30% of 12-24 year olds. There is evidence to suggest that smoking is addictive and, once hooked, young people find it hard to give up.

All advertisements for tobacco products contain health warnings. However, the tobacco industry has found more subtle ways of promoting their brands. They sponsor many major sports events such as cricket, motor racing and snooker. Those events gain a degree of exposure for their products which they could not buy through conventional advertising. Tobacco companies claim that their advertising is not intended to attract new smokers but to increase their individual share of the existing tobacco market.

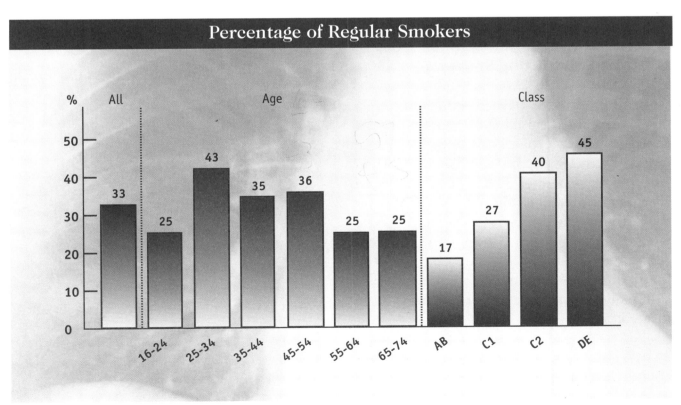

However, some believe that this argument is hard to accept. Logic suggests that as the product they are advertising may damage the health of many of their own customers, there is a need to recruit new smokers to replace those who have died or chosen to give up the habit. In 1999, the Government finalised plans to ban all tobacco advertising and sponsorship although 'Formula One' motor racing and professional snooker were given longer than other sports to find new sponsors.

Critics of successive governments have also suggested that they have ulterior motives for not placing greater restrictions on tobacco sales and advertising. Tobacco companies have given generous sums of money to political parties over the years. The Conservative Party received huge donations while they were in government. The new Labour Government became caught up in a controversy over tobacco advertising in 1997. 'Formula One' motor racing relies heavily on tobacco sponsorship. It was revealed that the head of 'Formula One', Bernie Eccleston, had made a £1 million pound donation to Labour Party funds shortly before it was announced that motor racing would be exempt from tighter restrictions on tobacco sponsorship. The Labour Party returned the money to avoid accusations of sleaze and favouritism.

Educating and Taxing Smokers

Governments have tried to educate people about the risks of smoking. Evidence suggests that the message has been accepted more readily by the upper and middle classes than working class people. It has been suggested that nicotine patches should be available on the National Health Service to help people who want to give up. These work by drip feeding small amounts of nicotine into the body, allowing smokers to gradually wean themselves off the habit that they have formed.

Another possible way of reducing smoking is to raise taxes on tobacco and cigarettes to a point where they can no longer be afforded. However, governments rely on the huge tax revenues from cigarette sales. They would be apprehensive to push the price too high in case massive numbers of people stopped smoking immediately. Such a development would make it difficult for any government to finance its spending priorities. The likely consequence is that money would then have to be raised in other ways such as increases in income tax and this would be likely to prove unpopular with voters.

Smoking is the single most important preventable cause of disease and premature death in Scotland. Each year, smoking accounts for 10,000 deaths - about one in six of all the deaths in Scotland. Smoking-related illness costs the NHS around £87 million each year.

The Dangers of Smoking

- Scottish deaths from lung cancer are amongst the highest in the world.
- Lung cancer is the single most common type of cancer in the country.
- Smoking is a major risk factor for coronary heart disease.
- Smoking is often a factor in chronic bronchitis, high blood pressure, strokes, peripheral vascular disease and a number of types of cancer and osteoporosis.
- Women who smoke are less likely to conceive.
- Women who smoke are more likely to lose their babies before or soon after birth.
- Children of smokers are more likely to be of small stature.
- Children of smokers are more likely to develop respiratory infections.

Amongst adults aged 25-64, the proportion who smoke has fallen from 40% in 1986 to 37% in 1996. However, this is still well above the Government's target of a figure of 32% by the year 2000. Smoking also increases a person's chances of being killed in a fatal fire. Of the 88 fire deaths in Scotland in 1996/97, 39 were caused by smoking.

Smoking Behaviour amongst Secondary School Pupils (1986-1996)

Year	Regular Smoker	Occasional Smoker	Tried Smoking
1986	13%	5%	24%
1990	13%	8%	22%
1992	11%	7%	23%
1994	12%	9%	23%
1996	14%	9%	23%

Diet

The link between diet and health is also well-established. In 1993, a Government Working Party produced 'The James Report' on Scotland's diet, confirming the poor balance of the Scottish diet and its damaging effect on the health of the population. Basically, the average Scottish diet is deficient in certain vitamins and fibre and contains too much saturated fat, sugar and salt. Children's diets are particularly bad with many eating little fruit and vegetables and some eating very substantial amounts of crisps, chips, snack foods, sweets and fizzy drinks.

Amongst the key findings stated in 'The James Report' were:

Selected Findings of 'The James Report'

- 28% of adults in Scotland eat fresh fruit once a week or less.
- 20% eat cooked green vegetables once a week or less.
- 34% eat cooked root vegetables once a week or less.
- 17% of adults living in Renfrew District eat less than one full meal per day.
- 24% of 15 year olds in the West of Scotland eat four or more snacks per day.

Unless Scottish people change their eating habits, the country is likely to retain one of the highest rates of mortality and disability from coronary heart disease, strokes and cancer and a lower life expectancy than most other Western countries. Poor diet also contributes to Scotland's poor dental health because of the large quantities of sugary foods consumed.

In 'The James Report', specific targets for the year 2005 were set down for Scotland's diet. Some of these are shown below:

'The James Report' Targets for 2005

Children

- All children over 2 years of age should eat 3-4 portions of vegetables and fruit per day.
- Whole grain or granary bread or cereals should be consumed twice daily.
- 75% of children over 2 years should consume semi-skimmed milk. Neither skimmed nor full-cream milk is recommended.
- 75% of children should eat fish twice weekly.
- 75% of children should eat meat products less than twice weekly.
- Confectionery consumption in children should fall by half.
- Adolescents, particularly those from disadvantaged areas, should be targeted to receive good dietary advice to ensure their own fitness for child-bearing and child-rearing and to ensure that good dietary practices are passed on to their children.

Adults

- All young men and women should eat three or more portions of vegetables and fruit per day.
- Fish should be eaten by 50% of the population twice per week.
- 85% of women and 70% of men should consume semi-skimmed or fully-skimmed milk.
- 50% of the bread eaten should be wholemeal or granary.
- Those eating fried food cooked in solid fat at home or in catering outlets should fall to 5% in adults aged 18-34 years and to 3% in those aged 35-59.
- Those eating chicken or other poultry twice per week should increase to 30% in both men and women.
- Those eating processed meat or meat-filled pies two or more times per week should fall to 30% in men aged 18-34 and to 20% in women of the same age. Only 20% of men and 10% of women aged 35-59 years are expected to persist with this dietary pattern.

Physical Exercise

Scotland's record for physical exercise is poor. Around one-third of all coronary heart disease and one-quarter of all strokes could be avoided if regular physical activity was undertaken by all. Programmes of physical activity can reduce mortality after a heart attack by 20% . Of those interviewed in the recent 'Scottish Health Survey', 53% of men and 62% of women acknowledged that they did not get sufficient regular exercise, while 23% of men and 26% of women undertook no moderate or physical activity in an average week.

Participation in sport and exercise has a significant impact on health standards. Over a period of many years, governments and local authorities have run 'Sport for All' campaigns and have tried to educate people about the benefits of exercise. However, many sports remain comparatively expensive and this

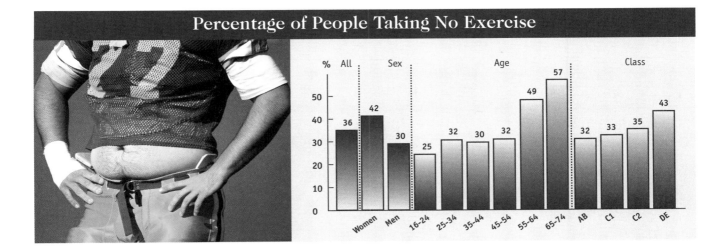

Percentage of People Taking No Exercise

prevents some people from taking part. The attractions of other leisure pursuits, including television and going to the pub, also prove too strong for many people.

Alcohol Misuse

Over 90% of the adult population use alcohol. It can be part of a healthy lifestyle if used in moderation. There is evidence of beneficial effects of moderate alcohol consumption by men over 40 and post-menopausal women. However, excessive consumption over a long period of time and 'binge drinking' are damaging to health, cause accidents and lead to anti-social behaviour.

The most recent 'General Household Survey' revealed that 8% of men and 1% of women in Scotland are drinking at levels which are definitely harmful. Scotland's statistics for drinking are not that much different from the rest of the UK except for one significant area – the extent of 'binge drinking'.

Particular concern has been expressed at the number of young people who are drinking and the quantity that they drink. Evidence suggests that alcohol consumption is habit-forming.

Some schools have reported problems of absenteeism amongst pupils as a result of drinking. There has been a steady increase in the number of young people (aged 12-15) drinking alcohol from 59% in 1990 to 64% in 1996. In addition, the average number of units drunk per week by young people of this age has more than doubled from 0.8 units in 1990 to 1.9 units in 1996. 'Alcopops' accounted for 18% of alcohol consumed by 12-15 year olds.

Harmful Health Effects of Drinking

- High blood pressure
- Increased chance of a stroke
- Increased chance of cancer of the mouth and throat
- Associated with mental breakdown
- Clear link to child abuse and domestic violence

Drug Misuse in Scotland

% by	All	Sex		Age					
		Women	Men	16-24	25-34	35-44	45-54	55-64	65-74
Ever Used	32	27	37	58	46	32	18	13	12
Used in past Year	14	10	17	35	15	12	5	5	7

Drug Misuse

All research suggests that drug misuse continues to escalate in Scotland. Surveys of young people regularly show that more than half of them claim to have taken an illegal substance at some time in their lives. Drug users find that their health can be affected in two different ways. Firstly, there are the direct risks associated with some forms of drugs use. In particular, the sharing of needles for injecting greatly increases the risk of HIV/ AIDS and hepatitis B and C. Dealers in Scotland frequently sell drugs that can kill, either because they are in too pure a form or because they contain potentially lethal impurities. There have been several widely publicised cases of young people dying after taking ecstasy tablets they had bought in pubs or clubs. Secondly, habitual drug users have to devote so much of their income to feeding their drug habit that they cannot afford to eat properly, with serious effects on their general health and wellbeing.

New Lifestyle Risks

In 1998, experts identified a link between the use of mobile phones and high blood pressure. It was claimed that one short conversation could have similar health effects to smoking two cigarettes and prolonged usage could lead to serious health problems such as heart attacks. According to this view, the electromagnetic field produced by the mobile phone causes arteries to narrow thereby increasing blood pressure. However, the research was not based on a large sample and a range of spokespersons for the communications industry refused to accept such claims. Nevertheless, by 1998 in the USA, seven people had taken out lawsuits against mobile phone companies, contending that use of their phones had led to tumours.

Working Conditions and Health

There are strict 'Health and Safety' laws that protect people's rights at work. However, it is clear that there are links between certain occupations and particular medical conditions.

Asbestos is recognised as one of the main man-made environmental hazards of the twentieth century. Those most at risk are workers who used asbestos in building contracts when it was widely used as an insulating material. Exposure to asbestos dust has a long-term effect that may take years to reveal itself. Many people who worked with asbestos have developed, much later in life, illnesses such as mesothelioma (a form of cancer) or asbestosis. The substance was used because it was cheap and effective, even though experts had been aware of its dangers for a long time. Many buildings erected in the 1950s and 60s contain large amounts of asbestos and dust can be released during refurbishment and renovation work. Many buildings have been demolished because of the expense that would be involved in making them safe by removing the asbestos insulation.

Former coal miners have also suffered because of exposure to danger. Some have respiratory diseases caused by exposure to dust and others have lost the use of their hands because of the constant effect of heavy vibrating coalcutting machinery.

Social Class and Health

To understand the link between social class and ill-health, it is necessary to be clear about what is meant by social class. Traditional definitions such as upper class, middle class and working class are of limited use in modern Britain. Social class is based on a mixture of factors including occupation, income level, housing and level of education. In official statistics, the definitions of social class used for many years have been based on the 'Registrar General's Classification'.

In a changing society, there are problems in using the 'Registrar General's Classification', most obviously because it is based on occupation. Although occupation is a reasonable indicator of a person's wealth, lifestyle and living conditions, it is difficult to classify people who are either unemployed or self-employed because they are not easily categorised in that way. Another procedure which seems outdated is that, when a woman marries, she is assumed to adopt the social class of her husband. In addition, the growing numbers of people over the age of 65 are not included in the 'Registrar General's Classification'. Consequently, a new 'Registrar General's Classification' has been developed.

The new classification is based not on skills but on employment conditions and relations, which are now considered to be vital in explaining the socio-economic conditions of modern society. This means that a job is placed in a category on the basis of a combination of status, pay level, amount of responsibility and skill level.

The Registrar General's Classification

Class	Title	Occupations	% of Population
I	Professional	Accountant, Lawyer, Doctor	5
II	Intermediate	Teacher, Managerial Workers	18
IIIa	Skilled Non Manual	Computer Operator, Skilled Clerical	12
IIIb	Skilled Manual	Electrician, Plumber, Lorry Driver	38
IV	Semi Skilled	Waiter / Waitress, Telephone Operator	18
V	Unskilled	Labourer, Cleaner	9

New Classification of Social Class

1. Higher managerial and professional occupations
   1.1 Employers and managers in larger organisations
   1.2 Higher professionals
2. Lower managerial and professional occupations
3. Intermediate occupations
4. Small employers and self-employed
5. Lower supervisory, craft and related occupations
6. Semi-routine occupations
7. Routine occupations
8. Long-term unemployed and those who have never worked

Source: 2001 Census of Population, the National Office of Statistics

The Link between Social Class and Health Standards

There have been four major reports which have studied the links between social class and health standards: 'The Black Report' (1980); 'The Health Divide' (1987); 'Working Together for a Healthier Scotland' (1998); 'The Acheson Report' (1998).

The Black Report (1980)

'The Black Report', published in 1980, was the first major attempt to analyse inequalities in health in the United Kingdom. The Labour Government (1974-1979) had set up a Research Working Group under the chairmanship of Sir Douglas Black to investigate the problem. Social Services Minister, David Ennals, had said in 1977 that:

"the crude differences in mortality rates between the various social classes are worrying ... the first step towards remedial action is to put together what is already known about the problem ... it is a major challenge for the next ten or more years to try to narrow the gap in health standards between different social classes."

By the time 'The Black Report' was published in 1980, a new Conservative Government was in power. The Report concluded that health standards were directly linked to social class and that this applied to all age groups. It argued that much of the problem was nothing to do with the National Health Service. Social and economic factors such as income level, unemployment, poor environment, poor education and sub-standard housing were the real causes of inequalities in health. The Report contained 37 specific recommendations but, in essence, there were two main policy areas. Firstly, it was suggested that there should be a major policy campaign aimed at reducing poverty in the United Kingdom and, secondly, that much more money should be spent on health education and the prevention of illness.

Key Findings of 'The Black Report'

The Causes of Inequalities in Health

income level
unemployment
poor environment
poor education
sub-standard housing

Political Solutions

campaign to reduce poverty
increased spending on health education
greater priority to prevention of illness

The new Conservative administration was unhappy with 'The Black Report'. Its publication was a low-key affair and only a small number of copies were distributed. The reasons for this were made clear in the foreword written by the new Secretary of State for Social Services, Patrick Jenkin:

"I must make it clear that additional expenditure on the scale which could result from the report's recommendations – the amount involved could be upwards of £2 billion per year – is quite unrealistic in the present or any foreseeable economic circumstances, quite apart from any judgement that may be formed of the effectiveness of such expenditure in dealing with the problems identified. I cannot, therefore, endorse the Group's recommendations. I am making the report available for discussion, but without any commitment by the Government to its proposals"

Government ministers went on to try and discredit 'The Black Report' by criticising it in three main ways.

Firstly, they said that the Report did not properly explain inequalities in health. It identified inequalities and gave evidence for their existence but, according to ministers, the explanations were flawed. Secondly, the Report had stated specifically that poorer people were less likely to make use of health services. The Government claimed to have evidence that this was wrong. Thirdly, the Government claimed that spending more money on health care would make no difference to health standards.

At this time, the priority of the Conservative Government was to reduce public spending. This allowed massive cuts in personal taxation and also led to the growth of more competition involving private health providers. Conservative politicians would have regarded 'The Black Report' as an old-fashioned socialist explanation for ill-health and the recommendations it made were opposite to their own political ideology.

The Health Divide (1987)

In January 1986, the Health Education Council (HEC) commissioned Margaret Whitehead to update the evidence on inequalities in health and to assess the progress made since the publication of 'The Black Report' six years previously.

The HEC was a 'quango', a body set up by the Government but theoretically independent in its work and policies. Shortly after commissioning this research, it was announced that the HEC was to be scrapped. Some MPs in the House of Commons claimed this was because the Government did not like what it was hearing from the HEC.

The work on inequalities in health would be embarrassing and the HEC were also campaigning strongly on alcohol, tobacco and diet issues which would upset some of the Government's financial backers. Drinks and tobacco manufacturers have often provided large donations to political party funds which some people regard as a sweetener to make sure government policies do not have a bad effect on these industries.

When 'The Health Divide' report was published, one week before the HEC was due to close down, a press conference was called to publicise the findings. It was cancelled, without explanation, one hour before it was due to start. It was claimed that an official from the Department of Health had put pressure on the Chairman of the HEC to cancel the conference because of the controversial nature of the conclusions in the report.

'The Health Divide' (also known as 'The Whitehead Report') revealed that the gap in health standards had actually widened since the publication of 'The Black Report'. It restated the direct link between health standards and social class. Published in 1987, a General Election year, it is perhaps little wonder that the Government was keen to suppress the findings of the Report which could have caused considerable political embarrassment.

Although 'The Black Report' and 'The Health Divide' both concentrated on social class as one of the main causes of inequalities in health, they acknowledged other factors. Further research has endorsed these findings.

Health and Deprivation: Inequality and the North

In 1988, a study was published entitled 'Health and Deprivation: Inequality and the North'. This examined the supposed inequalities in health standards between the North and South of Britain.

The Conservative Government of the time had been criticised for concentrating resources and attention on the South where most of their support was to the detriment of the North. This study concluded that even small variations in the level of deprivation between areas were reflected in variations in health standards.

Working Together for a Healthier Scotland (1998)

It was not until 1998, and the publication of 'Working Together for a Healthier Scotland', that the Government fully acknowledged the link between social class and ill health. In that consultation document, the following statement was made:

In 1980 'The Black Report' drew attention to the contribution of socio-economic inequalities (as indicated by social class) to inequalities in health experience within the UK. More affluent people of both sexes and at all ages experienced less illness and premature death than the disadvantaged groups. A class gradient was observed for most causes of death including stillbirth, accidents, cancers, respiratory diseases and cardiovascular disease, Available data indicated a similar pattern with regard to chronic illness.

Possible explanations for the relationship between health and inequality were considered, based on artefact, natural and social selection, culture or behaviour and economic and socio-structural factors. The Report stated that there was no single or simple explanation, but stressed the importance of material conditions of life....

Over the last 20 years or so, the gap in death rates between the most and least affluent categories has widened and a King's Fund publication in 1995 states that, in Britain, death rates were higher among disadvantaged social groups than among the more affluent, and the disadvantaged were likely to die about 8 years earlier.

Source: Working Together for a Healthier Scotland, Chapter 2

The publication of 'Working Together for a Healthier Scotland' in 1998 showed that evidence, from 'The Black Report' and 'The Whitehead Report', which clearly showed the link between social class and ill-health, was now being taken seriously. In his foreword to the Paper, the Secretary of State for Scotland said:

This Paper is about a twin challenge for Scots and for Scottish institutions. We can all act to improve our own lives, avoiding illness as we would accidents. Public and private bodies, Government, local authorities, agencies, companies can protect health through their policies, plans and actions.

Independent Inquiry into Inequalities in Health: The Acheson Report (1998)

This major study into inequalities in health, published in 1998, concluded that a sustained 10-year attack on the huge gap between the very richest and the very poorest is needed to improve the health of millions of Britons. It showed that poor men are 68% more likely to die in middle age than their richer counterparts, with poor women having a 55% greater risk of dying young. The mortality gap between rich and poor men had widened for coronary heart disease, strokes, lung cancer, accidents and suicide and, for women, for lung cancer and respiratory diseases.

Sir Donald Acheson, chairperson of the Inquiry, stated that health inequalities affect the whole of society and can be identified from foetus to old age. A key factor in low weight babies was a mother's birth weight and her pre-pregnant weight.

Selected Findings and Recommendations of 'The Acheson Report'

Selected Findings	Selected Recommendations
Children from poor families weigh on average 130 gms less than those from wealthy families	High priority should be given to reducing health inequalities in women of child-bearing age, expectant mothers and young children
Low birth weight plays a big part in infant mortality	Benefits should be increased in cash or in kind for women of childbearing age, expectant mothers, young children and older people
2.2 million British children are living at income levels of less than 50% of the national average (the EU definition of poverty)	Schools in poor areas should be given extra funding, with the local government Revenue Support Grant formula being amended so that it is more strongly weighted in favour of the poor
Infant mortality rate amongst the poor was 7 per 1000 in 1994-96	
Infant mortality rate amongst the upper social classes was 5 per 1000	Schools should provide free fruit, restrict unhealthy food, keep schools meals free and develop cooking skills
17% of professional men aged 45 to 64 said they had a long-term illness	A high quality public transport system should be developed which is affordable and includes concessionary fares for disadvantaged groups
48% of lower class men aged 45 to 64 said they had a long-term illness	
Health campaigns such as breast and cervical cancer screening have widened the health gap (the uptake is much higher amongst the upper social classes)	The Common Agricultural Policy should be reviewed so that surplus food redistributed to the poor can include fresh fruit and vegetables
More middle class people have given up smoking than working class people	Food companies should be encouraged to reduce salt content in processed food with no extra cost to the consumer
	Mothers should be encouraged to breastfeed their children
	Fluoride should be added to the water supply
	Tobacco advertising should be banned and nicotine patches should be provided on prescription on the NHS

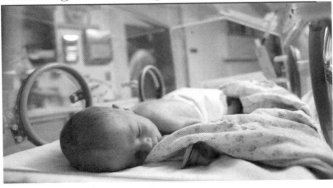

Living Longer and Enjoy Better Health

The basic conclusion is that the higher a person's social class, the more likely they are to live longer and enjoy better health. In technical terms, these are referred to as mortality and morbidity. Mortality refers to death rates while morbidity refers to levels of illness.

However, there are particular health problems which appear to be more common amongst higher social classes than lower social classes. This may be misleading. It is possible that more people from higher social classes than from lower social classes report certain forms of ill-health. For example, there are some forms of stress which are reported more by people with professional and managerial occupations than by those who are unemployed or with manual occupations. However, the stresses of living on a low income and with limited leisure opportunities can be every bit as serious as the stress associated with over-work and decision-making pressures.

Sociological Explanations for Social Class Inequalities in Health

Artefact
This links health to type of employment. In the 1940s, 50s and 60s, many people worked in jobs such as coal-mining, iron and steel making and other hard, physical work. Compared to thirty years ago, there are very few working class people today. Most of those who had working class jobs have now moved on to middle class jobs and enjoy better living standards and health. Although those in manual working class jobs still have poorer health, there are few people in this category.

Social Selection
This suggests that poor health and lack of ambition lead to unemployment or poor quality jobs. People in poor health, and those who are unambitious and who do not push themselves, tend to under-achieve and will finish up with poorer jobs or no job at all.

Behavioural Explanations
Lifestyle is the key factor in determining health standards. Our eating habits, drinking and smoking patterns, leisure activities and exercise regime all affect our health. People in better paid jobs have the money to make choices whereas people in poorly paid occupations do not have the same choice. Many people who have well-paid jobs also conform to the stereotype of a healthy lifestyle. They eat healthy foods, take exercise and probably consult their doctor at the first sign of ill-health. Those in less well-paid jobs tend to have a poorer diet, take less exercise and are less likely to consult medical specialists.

Environmental Explanations
Our working conditions and living environment determine our health standards. Individual behaviour cannot alter these factors. Basically, we are born as we are and cannot change. Although a minority of people agree with this explanation, most experts dismiss it and say that there is no evidence to back up this theory.

Gender and Health

Women have a greater life expectancy than men. Nowadays, in Scotland, women can expect to live five years longer than men, with average life expectancy for women moving towards 80. Seventy five percent of those alive over the age of 75 are women.

Mortality is greater in males at all ages. In childhood, the higher mortality rates for boys are because they are more likely to die from poisoning and injury. By the late teenage years, the mortality rates are even wider, partly due to the numbers of deaths from accidents.

This trend continues into early adulthood. Recent studies have shown that mortality rates for young women have declined in the last 20 years but for young men they have increased.

Across the whole of adult life, mortality rates are higher for men than women for all the major causes of death. These include cancers and heart disease. The specific cancers vary between the sexes. Breast cancer is the most common neoplasm amongst women while for men lung cancer is the most common.

However, it is interesting to see that women report more ill-health than men at all stages of their lives. The fact that women do report illness, rather than ignoring it, may contribute to the fact that they live longer. They are more likely to identify health problems at an early stage and have them diagnosed and treated while they can be cured. Men are much more reluctant than women to consult doctors and, for that reason, although they report less ill-health, they often have more serious health problems.

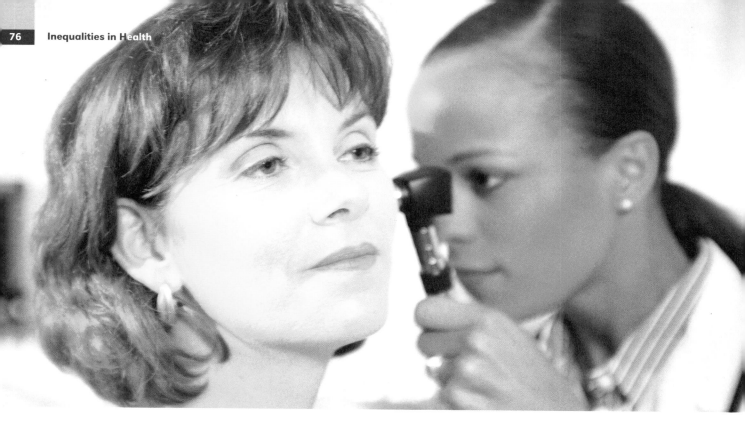

Women and Health

The physical differences between male and female account for some of the health differences between the sexes. Cancer of the reproductive system remains a constant threat to women. It can strike at any stage of their adult life leading to disfigurement, debility or death. Treatment can cause harrowing side-effects and is not always successful.

There is no easy way to prevent the cancers that affect women. Early detection of the condition makes the chances of successful treatment much higher, so screening programmes have been set up for both breast and cervical cancer. The aim is that every woman in vulnerable age groups should be screened at least every three years. For breast cancer, women aged 50 to 65 are specifically invited for a mammogram (breast x-ray) every three years. Older women can have a mammogram on request but it is not used with younger women because their denser breast tissue makes cancerous cells more difficult to detect. Instead, woman of all ages are encouraged to examine themselves regularly for breast lumps. Scientists have isolated genes that increase the likelihood of breast cancer and, if these are detected in a woman, she may be treated with tamoxifen, which acts as a preventive medicine.

Cervical cancer screening involves a smear test, normally carried out at a GP's surgery. A few cells are scraped from the cervix and sent for laboratory tests. These detect cancers at an early stage when they can usually be treated with lasers.

There have been recurring scares concerning the reliability of cancer screening. Patients in Inverclyde and Dundee, amongst others, have been recalled because of doubt about their test results. This has led to a loss of confidence in the system and may reduce the numbers of people taking tests.

Certain psychiatric conditions such as pre-menstrual syndrome and post-natal depression are obviously unique to women. However, in overall terms, they are less likely than men to be admitted to psychiatric hospitals. This is difficult to explain because women are much more likely than men to suffer from depression. Extra stress can be placed on a woman through her joint role as housewife and worker and from the fact that women are, on average, less well-off than men in financial terms.

During their childbearing years, the female body produces various hormones which assist the process of conception, pregnancy and birth. At the time of the menopause, when a woman ceases to be capable of reproduction, production of these hormones stops and their protective effects are lost.

Men and Health

Less attention has been paid to specific male conditions such as prostate and testicular cancer. However, in recent years, men have been given more information about these and have become more aware of symptoms and how to detect these cancers at an early stage.

Since the 1960s, there have been many campaigns and programmes aimed at highlighting women's health issues but less attention has been focused on the health needs of men. Given the growing divide in health standards between men and women, it would seem sensible that something should be done about this.

Some GPs have started to run 'Men's Health Clinics' in the same way as 'Well Woman Clinics' have sprung up over recent years. However, it can be difficult to persuade men to attend these clinics as many still have a macho mind-set that tells them going to the doctor is a sign of weakness.

Ethnic Origin and Health

More than five per cent of the British population are classed as belonging to ethnic minorities. This includes people of Indian, Pakistani, Bangladeshi and Caribbean origin. Many people, particularly those under the age of 30 whose families moved to Britain from Commonwealth countries for employment, are classed as ethnic minorities. In Scotland, the ethnic minority community is much smaller than in England, making up just over 1% of the population.

In health care terms, ethnic minority groups require specific consideration in two respects. Firstly, the NHS must ensure that no patient has any problem in accessing services because of their culture or language. Secondly, there are particular health patterns which apply to ethnic minorities and NHS services must be tailored to meet that need.

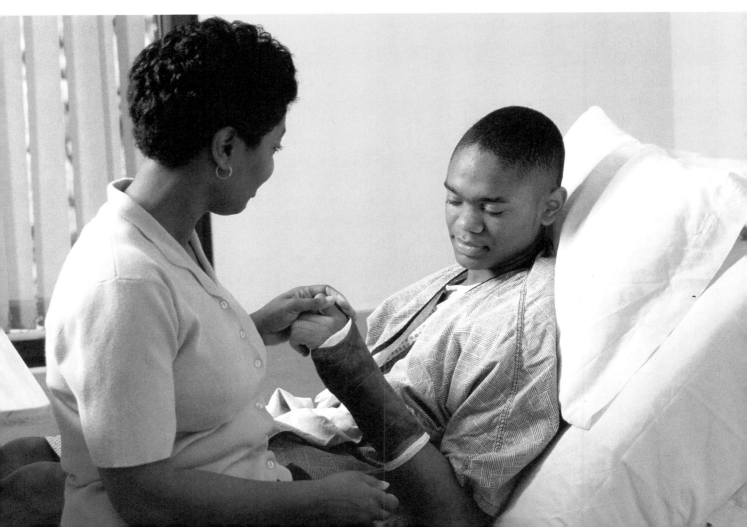

Access to Services

The issue of access to services was addressed in a report produced by the British Medical Association in 1995, entitled 'Multicultural Health Care: Current Practice and Future Policy in Medical Education'. This Report highlighted several points including that many NHS staff have inadequate training about health problems which particularly affect ethnic minorities. The Report also stated that some ethnic minority groups are reluctant to use medical services because they feel that they are not sensitive to their needs. This was especially true of female Muslim patients who would require to see a female gynaecologist. There was also a need for more interpreters to be employed to allow patients to talk to doctors and other staff.

Inequalities in Health

Overall, ethnic minorities in Britain have significantly poorer levels of health and a shorter life expectancy than the majority of the white population. This is usually explained in terms of occupation and income level. Many members of ethnic minorities in England and Wales are amongst the poorer members of the community.

Acquired and Inherited Illnesses

The health problems associated with ethnic minority groups can be divided into two types – acquired illnesses and inherited illnesses.

Acquired illnesses often result from visits to the country of origin, with diseases then being brought back to the UK. Malaria, hepatitis, tuberculosis and other illnesses can be brought into the country and may then spread quite quickly. In England, ethnic minority groups tend to be concentrated in inner-city areas and, amongst some communities, there may be a higher incidence of overcrowding which can lead to the rapid spread of disease.

Inherited illnesses can be specific to ethnic minority groups. The blood disorder, Thalassaemia (a form of anaemia), was particularly prevalent amongst the Cypriot community in Britain.

Perhaps the best example of an illness specific to one ethnic group is Sickle Cell Disease which affects the African and Caribbean population. Tay Sachs disease specifically affects the Jewish community.

Common Health Problems

There are different rates of incidence of common diseases and health problems amongst ethnic minorities compared to other population groups.

In Scotland, the most important of these is coronary heart disease (CHD). One of the biggest health problems in Scotland, the rate of CHD is even higher amongst people from the Indian ethnic group. Between 1979 and 1993, deaths from CHD amongst men and women born in the Indian sub-continent were respectively 36% and 46%. This was higher than the national average. Even at times when the national rate of CHD has fallen, the rate amongst people of Indian origin has risen.

Diabetes is also more common amongst people of Indian origin than in the rest of the population. People from an African-Caribbean background are less likely than average to suffer from CHD but they are more likely to suffer from hypertension and strokes. As a high proportion of people in the ethnic minority communities are young, these patterns could present particular problems in the future. When the people who are young today reach old age, there may be a far higher rate of CHD and strokes in areas with a large ethnic minority population.

Cancer is a further interesting example. Ethnic minority groups living in the UK display a lower rate of deaths from cancer than white Britons. However, the rate is higher than in countries such as India, Pakistan and in the Caribbean. The rate of cancer death amongst ethnic minorities in Britain is increasing, suggesting that some features of lifestyle in Britain contribute to the high number of cases.

Geographical Location and Health

Geographical location affects health standards on two levels. Macro-level patterns can be identified where there are higher rates of certain diseases in some parts of the country compared to others. Scotland, for example, is well-known for having a high rate of heart disease and dental problems. These patterns are partly related to socio-economic conditions in the area concerned.

Micro-level patterns are very localised. Studies have revealed significant clusters of leukaemia close to nuclear power installations. It has also been suggested that people who live very close to high-tension electricity cables are more likely to develop certain forms of cancer.

Considerable research has been carried out on the subject of childhood leukaemia. Cases of the disease, when plotted on maps, show clusters of cases in certain areas. Scientists and medical researchers have been unable to come up with a sure explanation for these clusters, but they offer two different alternatives.

Explanation 1

Location near Sources of Radiation.

Clusters have been identified close to both Sellafield and Dounreay, the two main nuclear research sites in the UK. Both of these sites have sustained accidents over the years, leading to the release of radiation. Clusters have also been found near sources of electromagnetic radiation such as electricity pylons and sub-stations. There have been unconfirmed reports of increased cases of childhood leukaemia close to radio and TV transmitters.

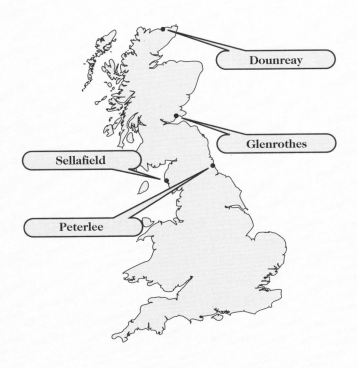

Explanation 2

Infection-based Spread of Childhood Leukaemia

Both Dounreay and Sellafield have an unusual population structure. Large numbers of people moved into what were previously rural areas at around the same time. Experts believe that this mixing of population leads to a higher risk of infection. They have observed this pattern in three different sets of circumstances.

Firstly, at large new industrial complexes – such as the nuclear research plants at Dounreay and Sellafield and at North Sea oil installations such as at Sullum Voe in Shetland – there are notable excesses of childhood leukaemia cases.

Secondly, the same pattern is found in New Towns built in mainly rural areas. Studies of Glenrothes (Fife), Peterlee (near Newcastle) and Corby (East Midlands) have shown clusters of the disease.

Thirdly, study of historical records shows that areas that received large numbers of war-time evacuees had much higher than average rates of childhood leukaemia. All three sets of circumstances point to the mixing of population groups as contributing to an infection-based cluster of the disease.

Health Inequalities: Glasgow

In December 1999, a controversial survey undertaken by the Townsend Centre for International Poverty Research presented evidence that Glasgow has the worst record of any British city for early death, infant mortality rates and long-term illnesses.

For example, people in the Shettleston area of Glasgow are 3.4 times more likely to die before the age of 65 than those living in Wokingham, Woodspring and Romsey, the healthiest areas of South-East England. In addition, within Glasgow's Anniesland constituency, which includes Drumchapel, infant mortality rates at 103 deaths per 10,000 births in the first year of life are twice as high as those in Esher and Walton in Surrey (51.6 deaths per 10,000 births). Research has

shown that of the nine poorest health areas in Britain all are in Glasgow and the West of Scotland.

In attempting to address this and other issues relating to health inequality, the recent report produced by Sir John Arbuthnott ('The Arbuthnott Report') proposed a new formula for allocating resources between Scottish health boards. According to the "The Arbuthnott Report', communities such as Glasgow with high levels of deprivation should receive a greater share of NHS resources.

However, a number of commentators have pointed out that this new formula for allocating resources may not be sufficient to greatly improve Glasgow's health record.

They argue that bad social and economic conditions such as poor housing, unemployment and restricted educational opportunities are the root cause of much ill health and that they must be addressed if real progress is to be made.

Glasgow's position as the sickest city in Scotland and one of the worst in Britain was confirmed in February 2000 by the publication of research by the King's Fund.

A survey of 120 health authority areas in the UK put Glasgow at 114th place, based on the number of deaths from heart disease, cancer and avoidable illnesses like asthma and tuberculosis as well as on the length of hospital waiting lists.

Health Authority Rankings

Health Board	Rank (out of 120)
Argyll and Clyde	93
Ayrshire and Arran	81
Borders	18
Dumfries and Galloway	15
Fife	37
Forth Valley	53
Greater Glasgow	114
Highland	9
Lanarkshire	96
Lothian	62
Orkney	6
Shetland	59
Tayside	41
Western Isles	67

Source: The King's Fund

STUDY TOPIC 2

In what ways does society meet the health care needs of the elderly?

Introduction

Up until the late 20th century, the life cycle for many people in Britain was very predictable: they were born, they went to school, they got a job, they retired and they died. All of these events happened in fairly quick succession to each other. Towards the end of the 20th century, this pattern began to change. People now live longer than ever before and they are likely to retire at an earlier age. This means that many have a comparatively long period of retirement. Indeed, the fact that pensioners make up 17.8% of the population in Scotland, compared to schoolchildren who make up 14%, is a statistic which demonstrates demographic change, one which has important consequences for the provision of health care.

The 'Patients' Charter' is specific about the importance of equal access to health care: *"You have the right to receive health care on the basis of your clinical need, not on your ability to pay, your lifestyle, or any other factor."* The General Medical Council's code of good practice upholds this principle as does the British Medical Association (BMA). Rationing by age is wrong although rationing according to the ability to benefit is justified. No one should be excluded from health treatment on age grounds alone because ageing does not happen at a uniform rate. What is needed in a health service which has to ration its limited resources is the development of 'biological' rather than 'chronological' indicators on the potential benefits of treatment.

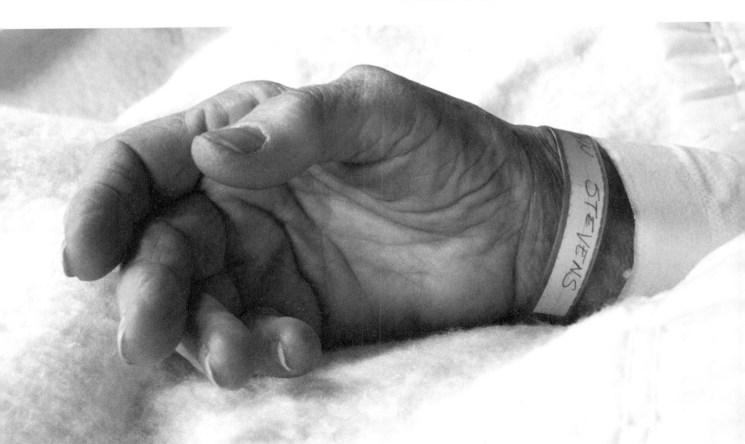

Rationing Health Care – Age Discrimination

In 1999, The Guardian reported that a Gallup poll of 1,600 people over 50 found 1 in 20 felt they had been refused treatment on the grounds of their age, and 1 in 10 felt they had been treated differently since reaching 50. In response, Age Concern, the pressure group which commissioned the Gallup survey, appealed to the public and to health professionals for more evidence about age discrimination in the National Health Service. Over 1,000 people responded. The report published revealed that people over 50 faced barriers obtaining treatment, a less caring attitude amongst some health staff and a fear of complaining by patients.

As a result, Age Concern has demanded urgent government action in relation to age discrimination. The organisation said that age discrimination was widespread, from top teaching hospitals to GPs. *"The Government must act now to halt the spread of the national epidemic of ageism in the NHS,"* said Sally Greengross, Director General of Age Concern. The charity's survey, commissioned this year, found that one in 20 people over 65 had been refused NHS treatment.

The charity was particularly concerned about women aged 65 or over who are not routinely invited for breast screening, even though 63% of all deaths from breast cancer occur in this age group. Similarly, although 66% of heart attacks involve people aged 65 or over, 20% of coronary care units operate an age-related admissions policy. Also, 40% of units attach age restrictions to the use of clot-busting drugs. Age Concern claimed that there is a national policy to refuse NHS heart transplants to any patient over 60.

Although both the Royal College of Physicians and the Medical Research Council have conceded that age discrimination within the NHS has become a significant problem, a Department of Health spokesperson said the Government would not tolerate discrimination of any kind in health care. Indeed, the number of women over 65 requesting breast screening had doubled since 1994.

The Gender Gap

Women live longer than men. Why is this so? The fact that this difference in life expectancy is universal to all countries and societies suggests that it is caused by in-built genetic differences. However, it should also be noted that, in the UK, women report more illness throughout their life and make more use of medical services. This will improve their chances of living to an older age.

There is some evidence to suggest that geographical location also has an effect on life expectancy. Mountain environments appear to promote long-life. In the small state of Andorra on the borders of France and Spain, the average life expectancy is 86 for men and 95 for women. The combination of better air quality and a diet which is based on fresh local produce has helped to create the conditions that encourage longevity over a large number of generations.

The Ageing Process

The length of time that a person lives is determined by a number of factors, only some of which can be influenced by him or herself. The process begins before birth with the health and nutritional status of expectant mothers. Those with a poor diet or who smoke or drink are more likely to give birth to weaker children.

Throughout their life, people can make decisions which will improve their chances of a long life. However, this is a generalisation. There are too many examples of fit and healthy people who die suddenly at a young age and of chain-smoking, overweight drinkers who live to their 80s for it to be anything else! Sensible eating and drinking habits, regular exercise and general care and attention to the body will promote good health and the likelihood of living to a good age.

Ageing begins at a comparatively early age. As the body gets older, it becomes less efficient at repairing damage. Muscle power fades, the nervous system and the senses lose their efficiency, the skin becomes less supple and bones more brittle and the arteries harden. As the damage accumulates, more strain is placed on vital organs which can fail and lead to death.

Taking the Medicine

Modern medicine is able to compensate for many of these changes. Many elderly people are only alive because they have had life-saving surgery or because they depend on medication. It is possible for people's bodies to be kept functioning long after their mental faculties have deteriorated to the point where they cannot really look after themselves. The life cycle for many elderly people ends as it began: as a relatively helpless individual, relying heavily on others to meet their basic needs such as eating, dressing, washing and so on. Just as a baby has all major and minor decisions made for it, the same is true for many very elderly people. The life cycle has gone full circle.

Elderly People in the UK
1,035,228 people aged 60 and over (59% women, 41% men)
913,808 people over the state retirement age
people aged 75 and over (67% women, 33% men)
people aged 85 and over in Scotland (76% women, 24% men)

Living Longer

There are more than 10 million pensioners living in the United Kingdom. This fact has important implications for policy makers who plan to take care of the needs of elderly people. Of particular significance is the fact that the number of people in the UK aged 75 and over is likely to rise from 4 million in 1994 to 6.8 million in 2034. Indeed, in the same period, the number of people aged over the current state retirement age is projected to rise by more than 50%. Clearly, there is a need for the country to plan for these demographic changes.

This will be a major challenge as the ratio of working age people to pensioners in the UK is set to decline into the next century. The current ratio is 3.4 people of working age to each pensioner; by 2040 it will be 2.3 people of working age to each pensioner (allowing for the equalisation of the state pension age at 65).

In Scotland, the population aged over 75 increased from 315,000 in 1987 to 339,000 in 1997, and it is projected to rise to 379,000 in 2012. Over the same period, the numbers over 85 years of age, who are the main users of health and care services, increased from 60,000 to 79,000 and is projected to rise to 97,000 in 2012.

Average Life Expectancy

In 1996, there were 9,400 people (1,440 men and 7,960 women) aged 100 and over. It is estimated that, by 2031, there will be 34,000 (28,000 women and 6,000 men).

In the 1950s, the average life expectancy for people in Britain was 67 for men and 72 for women. By 1997, this had increased to 74 for men and 79 for women. People who live to the age of 72 stand a very good chance of surviving into their 80s. These figures place Britain high up in a world league table of life expectancy, although, in European terms, it is comparatively low.

Income, Retirement Pensions and State Benefits

Since research suggests that there are important links between income and health, the income of pensioners is significant. Research from Age Concern suggests that a single pensioner needs at least £125 per week on which to live.

Social Security expenditure on benefits for older people has grown from £27 billion in 1979/80 to £41 billion in 1996/97. However, this is a declining proportion of the total Social Security budget, dropping from 54% to 44%. 80% of Social Security spending on the elderly is on retirement pensions. The remainder is largely on income support and housing benefit. As the elderly make up a growing proportion of the UK population and as people live to older ages, the commitment to spending on the elderly will increase. The number of dependent people (those who rely on pensions and benefits) will increase in proportion to the number of people who are

Average Life Expectancy in Selected European Countries (1997)

	Male	Female
Belgium	74	81
France	75	83
Germany	73	79
Iceland	78	83
Italy	75	82
Netherlands	75	81
Spain	75	82
Sweden	76	81
UK	74	79

Average Life Expectancy in Selected Countries Worldwide (1996)

USA	76
Mexico	72
Brazil	67
UK	77
France	79
Bulgaria	71
India	62
Malaysia	72
Japan	80
Egypt	65
Ghana	57
Zambia	43
Sierra Leone	37

working and paying money into the system at present through taxes.

The single person's pension is £66.75 per week and a couple's £106.70 (at January 2000). This might be compared to average weekly earnings which are £367.60. This means that a single person's pension is currently 17.6% of average earnings and a couple's 28.%. A single person's pension of 30% of average earnings would be £110.28. A couple's pension of 50% of average earnings would be £183.80.

Pensions used to be increased in line with earnings or prices, whichever was the greater. In November 1979, this link was broken and pensions now correspond to prices. Had pensions continued to parallel earnings, a single person's pension would be £89.60 in April 1998 and a couple's £143.40. A single pensioner, therefore, is losing £24.90 per week and a couple £40 per week.

Occupational Pensions

About two thirds of today's pensioners have an occupational pension. An occupational pension is an additional pension which many people take out while they are working. They pay extra every month and, when they retire, they get a lump sum payment and then a monthly pension until they die. Although an increasing number of women have pensions, these tend to be lower than men's. Many women rely on their partner's pension to provide an adequate income in retirement.

Household Spending

In the UK, households spend on average 38.2% of their incomes on housing, fuel and food. However, where the head of a household is aged 65 and over, a higher proportion of money is spent each week on these (41.5% of expenditure). This proportion is even greater for pensioners living alone who are mainly dependent on state pensions - 52.8% of their expenditure goes on housing, fuel and food.

Elderly people who are mainly dependent on state pensions and are living alone experience other inequalities. For example, a single pensioner household is less likely to own consumer durables (e.g. a video recorder, freezer or microwave) than a pensioner household comprising two or more people. A similar pattern is shown in statistics for the ownership of telephones and washing machines: 87% of pensioners have a telephone, compared to 92% of all households; 69% have a washing machine, compared to 90% of all households.

Christmas Bonus

All pensioners receive the £10 Christmas Bonus. This has not been increased since its introduction in 1972. Had it been increased in line with prices it would be £70.80 at December 1998 and more (£120.30) if increased in line with earnings.

A Widening Gap

State benefits form a small part of the income of the richest pensioners but a major part for the poorest. Some interesting statistics illustrate this divide. 62% of pensioners in Scotland have incomes too low to pay income tax. 28% of pensioners in the UK do not have a bank account. One of the most important consequences of low income is that health care for elderly people in the United Kingdom is likely to be provided by the public rather than by the private sector.

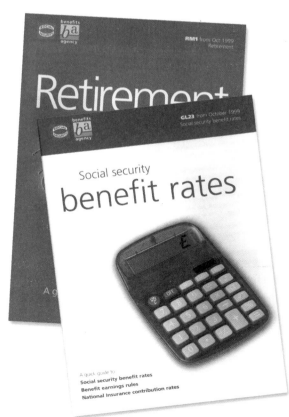

Health Problems of Elderly People

Many elderly people are very fit and mobile and require virtually no care at all. However, others are very dependent on other people, requiring anything up to round-the-clock attention. People who need long-term NHS care can be divided into various categories.

Some elderly people suffer from hereditary or congenital illnesses or conditions. These normally necessitate extensive health care for the rest of their lives. This could require tube feeding, physiotherapy and exercise therapy, continence care or the specialised medical and social support needed by Haemophiliacs.

Others experience an acute episode or illness, such as an accident or stroke, which causes short-term or long-term care needs. The dividing line may not be clear when the hospital wishes to end in-patient care. This situation can be difficult for elderly people who may not have relatives who are able to provide continuing care during recovery at home.

There are also problems for some who endure a long-term chronic disability such as that caused by arthritis or multiple sclerosis. Some conditions remain relatively stable, others will come and go and others again will slowly but surely deteriorate.

Some forms of mental illness may require regular or intermittent periods of residential treatment, perhaps treatable by a combination of drugs, therapy and social support. Neurological conditions, such as Parkinson's Disease or multiple sclerosis, require a high level of drug monitoring, combined with nursing and social support. Alzheimer's Disease involves a progressive decline in mental capacity and is accompanied by physical deterioration and behavioural change. AIDS / HIV requires both medical and social support and the ability to move from home to a supported setting and back again. Other dilemmas may occur with terminally patients with illnesses such as cancer.

Dementia and Alzheimer's Disease

Recent estimates suggest that over 700,000 people in the UK currently suffer from dementia, with more than 60,000 in Scotland. Dementia is a condition brought on by different illnesses that affect the brain. The prevalence of dementia increases with age. 1 in 1000 people aged 40-65 suffers from dementia, 1 in 50 aged 65-70, 1 in 20 aged 70-80, and 1 in 5 aged 80 and above.

There are different illnesses that can cause dementia but the most common of these is Alzheimer's Disease. 55% of people suffering from dementia have Alzheimer's Disease. This is a physical disease which attacks the brain cells that store memory and the brain nerves and transmitters that carry instructions around the brain. There is evidence to suggest that the likelihood of suffering from Alzheimer's Disease is influenced by genetic factors.

The disease typically begins with lapses of memory, mood swings and difficulty in finding the right words. Later, the person will probably become more confused and find it difficult to understand what is being said. Sufferers undergo personality changes, appearing to no longer care about those around them and becoming irritable and apathetic.

Eventually, they may suffer mood swings and burst into tears for no apparent reason or become convinced that people are trying to harm them. They may adopt irrational behaviour like wandering from their home and becoming lost, undressing in public and making inappropriate sexual advances.

They may become totally dependent on others as their personality disintegrates. There is no cure for the disease but treatments are being developed which can hold or improve the symptoms for a few months in the mild to moderate stages.

Changing Medical Technology and the Elderly

The main reasons for the growing number of elderly people are improved health standards, housing and working conditions over their lifetime. However, there are some new treatments and technologies which have become available that can prolong life not just for elderly people but for all ages. Some of these are applied most often to older people, while some are given mainly to younger people.

Heart Surgery
By-pass surgery is quite routine nowadays and can prolong life. Many people who might have died of heart disease in their forties and fifties now live to old age because of this surgery.

Cataract Surgery
Some eyesight problems can be cured through cataract surgery. This has reduced the number of elderly blind people who become dependent on others to meet their needs.

Replacement Hips / Joints
Hip and / or knee replacement surgery can greatly improve the lifestyle for elderly people who have mobility problems. Replacement joints are designed to last for twenty years or more. Some very old people, notably the Queen Mother, have had a replacement for the replacement fitted.

There are many devices available that make it easier for elderly people to live on their own. These gadgets can help to overcome health problems. In the past, some elderly people may have needed to be taken into 'residential care' but the development of technology allows them to remain in the community.

Chair Lifts
Two storey houses can be fitted with a chair lift to allow someone to move up and down stairs easily.

Bath Lifts / Hoists
Bathrooms can be fitted with different types of hoist or lift to help elderly people get in and out of the bath.

Alarm Systems
Homes can be connected to alarm systems that bring the person into contact with a telephone operator. Many local authorities operate this system for elderly people. A simpler form of alarm switches on a light on the outside of the house to show that the elderly person requires help.

Tracking Devices
These have been developed in Japan and the USA. Elderly people wear a bracelet with a microchip which allows them to be tracked. This is useful for people in the earlier stages of Alzheimer's Disease. In theory, the chips could be implanted in the same way as pets can be tagged.

The Role of the Independent Sector

Voluntary Services

The voluntary sector plays a variety of roles in meeting the needs of elderly people. Housing Associations are mainly voluntary organisations, most of which also have charitable status. They provide specialised and general needs accommodation. Specialised housing includes 'sheltered housing', very 'sheltered housing' and homes specially adapted to specific physical needs. General needs housing provides suitable homes for older people who often want to be in locations close to shops and services and in small housing units.

Personal care is also provided though the voluntary sector. The Macmillan Nursing organisation, Age Concern and the Marie Curie Fund provide voluntary nursing services, including day-care and night-sitting services. Voluntary organisations, including the Women's Royal Voluntary Service (WRVS), are also involved in the provision of home helps, 'meals on wheels' and lunch clubs and outings for elderly people. Some, such as local Age Concern branches, also organise car services for elderly people to take them shopping.

The Private Sector

Private care, like voluntary organisations, existed before the start of the National Health Service when wealthy people could afford to employ their own nursing and care staff. The role of the private sector declined when the NHS was established in 1948. However, the 1980s and 1990s saw a major growth in private services, encouraged by the Conservative Governments of the time.

The growth of private residential homes for elderly people in the 1980s was spectacular. Many people saw it as a very good investment. Some professional footballers even invested their signing on fees and bonuses in residential homes.

At that time, the Department of Social Security met the bill for private 'residential care' but the mounting cost to the Government was one of the main reasons for introducing 'Community Care'.

Since the start of 'Community Care', there has been a tighter rein on finance but the private sector has still been encouraged to play a bigger role in the 'mixed economy of care'. In particular, private home visiting care agencies have grown, especially in England and Wales. Social Services departments (Social Work in Scotland), in their role as enablers, often hire private agencies to provide care services. Local authorities may also employ private companies to meet other care needs of elderly people as part of their wider policy of privatisation. One further area in which the private sector has grown, although not strictly health-related, is in the provision of private pension funds and schemes.

Caring for the Elderly

The level of health care which a person needs depends on how dependent they are. Dependent and independent are two extremes. People vary from being completely independent (i.e., they can do everything for themselves) to being completely dependent (i.e., they can do nothing for themselves). The level of dependency of an elderly person is assessed by judging them against their ability to carry out various activities.

Dependency Criteria
Feeding
Having a bath
Dressing
Going to the toilet
Cooking
Climbing stairs
Getting into and out of bed
Going shopping

The vast majority of older people can perform most of these tasks themselves. However, the minority who cannot look after themselves place a heavy burden of dependency on others. Depending upon individual circumstances, the burden of looking after dependent elderly people may fall on the family or on the state.

There are no totally reliable statistics on how many people require care of some kind in Britain. Some estimates put the figure as high as ten million. The vast majority of these people receive informal care from members of their family, friends and neighbours. This informal care sector is difficult to quantify but it probably saves the NHS millions of pounds every year.

The state – in the form of the UK Parliament, the Scottish Parliament or local authorities (usually Social Work departments) – intervenes to provide care for many people. This care can range from 'day care' to 'residential care' and 'Community Care'.

Day Care, Residential Care and Community Care

Day Care

'Day care' for elderly people in Scotland can take many different forms. Hospitals or community centres can provide a range of services including leisure pursuits, medical attention and welfare advice. Voluntary organisations can offer lunch, bingo and tea dances. The number of 'day care' patients and recipients of home help services has increased steadily over the period from the late 1980s to the early 1990s. However, between 1993 and 1997, the number fell by 400, possibly as a result of financial cutbacks from local authorities. There has been a modest increase in the number of 'meals on wheels' provided. It is now over 2.5 million per year but the numbers of meals served in lunch clubs has declined.

'Residential care' involves receiving round-the-clock attention and, normally, living full-time in a hospital, care home, nursing home or other similar place. 'Community Care' involves a person living in their own home with the support of the community (relatives, friends, neighbours) complemented by a few hours of home help time per week and the delivery of 'meals on wheels'.

Residential Care

Residential care can be provided by the state or by private companies. All residential homes must be inspected regularly to ensure that they conform to the highest standards. Residential homes try to meet all care needs within one building, have well-trained staff and offer residents the company of other elderly people. Some critics say that this is very expensive for the individual, their family or the state (£300 per week upwards) and suggest that life is impersonal, lacks privacy and is dictated by routine.

For some people, 'Community Care' is no longer an option. They are totally unable to look after themselves, do not have family readily available to help them and they may even present a danger to themselves or people who live around them. At this point, a person will normally be taken into 'residential care'.

The Wagner Report, 'A Positive Choice', published in 1988, was a study of 'residential care services'. Its conclusions were not positive. Evidence suggested that the service was demoralised and that there were many cases of insensitivity and examples of cruelty.

Day Care for Elderly People in Scotland (1980-1997)

	1980	1991	1993	1995	1997
Day Centres					
Total number of day centre places	3,625	7,715	8,280	8,336	7,309
Total number of day centre places per 1000 people aged 65+	5.0	10.0	10.7	10.7	9.3
Home Helps					
Number of home help clients	60,703	85,728	88,038	93,471	83,616
Number of home help clients per 1000 people aged 65+	83.9	111.5	114.0	120.2	106.9
Average number of clients per home help	6.3	8.0	8.0	8.3	8.0
Lunch Clubs					
Number of meals served per club	4,327	2,731	2,961	2,658	2,007
Meals on Wheels					
Number of meals served	1,863	2,164	2,335	2,237	2,466
Average number of meals served per 1000 people aged 65+	2,575	2,814	3,022	2,877	3,241

Source: Adapted from Community Care, Scotland 1997

The Report itself gained little publicity and it was overtaken by developments in 'Community Care' following the publication of 'The Griffiths Report'.

Functions of Residential Homes
Long-term Care
Respite Care - look after people, who are normally cared for at home, for short periods in order to give their carers a break
Convalescence - for people recovering from illness
Hospice - for those suffering terminal illness

Source: Adapted from the Wagner Report

Providers of Residential Care

The four main providers of 'residential care' are the local authorities, the voluntary sector, the private sector and the National Health Service.

The Providers of Residential Care
Local Authorities
Voluntary Sector
Private Sector
National Health Service

The National Assistance Act of 1948 required each local authority to provide residential accommodation for persons who by reason of age, infirmity or any other circumstance were in need of care and attention which was not otherwise available to them. Provision by the voluntary sector has grown as 'Community Care' has grown. In some cases, voluntary organisations have taken over homes run by local authorities. In other cases, they run their own homes, sometimes specialising with particular client groups.

Although the National Health Service still provides accommodation for people who have long-term illnesses or mental problems, the Government is trying to shift the responsibility for people who need 'social care' rather than 'medical care' to local authorities, private companies or the voluntary sector. Health authorities claim that they cannot treat many elderly people therefore they should not be their responsibility. Local authorities say that they have no money to provide or pay for 'residential care' for these same people. This leads to the problem of 'bed blocking', where beds in NHS hospitals are taken up by elderly patients who have nowhere else to go, who cannot be treated and who simply have their symptoms alleviated.

Warehousing, Horticulture and Normalisation

There are different theories as to how people in care should be treated. These are known as 'warehousing', 'horticulture' and 'normalisation'.

'Warehousing' is the type of accommodation where people are simply housed and their immediate needs are met. Individual circumstances and demands are seldom considered. The residents are all treated the same. In many respects, some critics argue that this type of accommodation resembles a prison.

The 'horticulture' approach tries to nurture the full capabilities of each individual. This approach is used less with elderly people and more with the physically and mentally handicapped.

'Normalisation' is the situation where people are given support and help but are still expected to integrate as much as possible into everyday normal life. This approach is closest to the philosophy of 'Community Care'.

Care of Older People in Scotland (1980-1997)

Residential Accommodation	1980	1991	1993	1995	1997
Residential Care Homes					
Number of residential places	14,409	18,171	17,920	16,998	16,527
Number of places per					
1000 people aged 75+	54	55	56	52	49
Ratio of places					
(LA: Private: Voluntary)	65: 1: 34	53: 24: 23	51: 25: 24	49: 27: 23	47: 28: 25
Sheltered Housing					
Number of dwellings	8,476	312,550	33,190	34,385	36,847
Number of dwellings per					
1000 people aged 65+	12	41	43	44	47
Private Nursing Homes					
Number of places	n/a	11,898	16,477	19,020	22,831

Source: Adapted from Community Care, Scotland 1997

Some Criticisms

While 'residential care' is often appropriate, sensitively administered and desirable, it has sometimes had a poor press. Recently, reports have suggested that some people who are taken into this type of care are unaware of their circumstances. Also, stories of maltreatment of elderly people occasionally hit the headlines.

Ill-treatment is often caused by a lack of resources and inadequate training for staff and management in the homes. The other main criticism of 'residential care' is the poor facilities and buildings. Again, this is not a criticism of the carers specifically but a condemnation of the lack of resources available to maintain decent standards.

Community Care

'Community Care', where the person remains within the community (usually in his or her own home), has a variety of forms but is based on the notion that individuals have their own 'Personal Care Plan'. This lists all their needs and who will help to meet them. Very often, individuals can meet many of their own needs, e.g., by cooking for themselves, but may require particular support, e.g., dressing of wounds. From the point of view of the state, 'Community Care' is often a cheaper option than 'residential care'. Having said that, it can place a major financial burden on local authorities which have to provide home helps. Some argue that the burden is often so great, some deserving individuals do not receive the quality of care they need.

This leads to criticisms where, it is alleged, some elderly people are abandoned in their homes when they really cannot meet many of their own needs. In cases like this, it may also make some people feel isolated if they have no family nearby.

For many people, the reality is that they are in a continuum of care where the dividing line between 'residential care' and 'Community Care' is hard to define.

Development of Care in the Community

Traditionally, Scotland had a policy of 'institutionalisation'. People were taken out of the community and placed in institutions where their needs could be addressed. The level of 'institutionalisation' in Scotland was always higher than in the rest of the UK. In the mid 1980s, Scotland had twice as many psychiatric in-patients per head of population and more than one and a half times as many mentally handicapped patients as the rest of the UK. A study in the late 1970s showed that Scotland had 15 geriatric beds per 1000 population compared to 9 in England and Wales. Health service spending in Scotland was heavily weighted towards hospital services rather than towards community services.

It is difficult to be confident of the reasons why Scotland had this tradition of 'institutional care'. It may date from the formation of the National Health Service in the 1948 and the strong position of the Labour Party in Scotland, with its influence on decision-making and its inclination towards state provision. Until the latter part of the 1980s, private sector involvement in health care in Scotland had been limited although the voluntary sector had made a contribution.

In 1986, the then Secretary of State for Social Services asked Sir Roy Griffiths, the Managing Director of the Sainsbury supermarket chain, to examine the way in which public funds were used to support 'Community Care' and advise on ways in which 'Community Care' could be made more effective and efficient. His report, 'Community Care: Agenda for Action', was published in 1988. It was to prove very influential in the development of 'Community Care' policies. 'Griffiths' was critical of the way 'Community Care' operated and was particularly concerned about the lack of a clear-cut division of responsibilities between health boards, social work departments, housing departments and the voluntary and private sectors.

'Griffiths' made three main recommendations:

■ The Government should appoint a minister with specific responsibility for 'Community Care' to make the best use of resources and to monitor progress.

■ Local council social work departments should take the lead role in identifying the needs of patients, creating packages of care and co-ordinating services.

■ Those referred to nursing homes and 'residential care' should be evaluated by social workers to establish if they really needed 'residential care' and to assess their financial circumstances to see if they could contribute to the cost of care.

The policy known as 'Community Care' applies to services for the elderly, mentally ill and people with learning difficulties. Over many years, these services were known within health care circles as the 'Cinderella services' because they were given so little attention.

The origins of 'Community Care' date back to the 1950s and 60s. At that time, there was a shift in attitudes concerning how society should care for the mentally ill, and some of the old Victorian asylums were closed. The new philosophy said that asylums were no longer appropriate. Instead, services and support should be provided in people's own homes, giving the person as much independence as possible. There was an explosion of 'Community Care' from the late 1980s onwards into other branches of health care such as meeting the needs of elderly people.

Arrangers, Purchasers or Providers?

'Community Care' promoted a more 'mixed economy' of care with contributions from the public, private and voluntary sectors. 'Griffiths' himself stated that social service authorities should see themselves as the arrangers and purchasers of care services, not as mono-polistic providers.

This statement reaches the heart of what 'Community Care' policies were about. As well as changing the way in which vulnerable people would be looked after, 'Community Care' fitted in with the ideology of the Conservative Government, who had introduced private sector values and a competitive ethos to many policy areas. The creation of the internal market in health care was part of this, as was the privatisation of state-owned utilities such as electricity, gas and telecommunications.

Furthermore, the costs of keeping enormous numbers of elderly people in residential accommodation worried a government that was committed to keeping public spending down. The cost of social security benefits for people in residential accommodation had risen from £25 million per year in the late 1970s to over £1.5 billion in the late 1980s.

Finally, the Government was well aware of the projected demographic changes that would see a large increase in the numbers and proportion of very old people in the UK population.

Caring for People

The Government responded to 'The Griffiths Report' by producing their own White Paper, 'Caring for People' (November 1989). The reason for the delay is thought to have been that the Prime Minister had reservations about giving a key role to local authority social work departments. Many local authorities were Labour-controlled at the time and the prospect of giving them a lead role worried the Prime Minister. The Conservative Government of the time, under Margaret Thatcher, had dismantled many other powers of local authorities.

The White Paper suggested five main changes:

- The 'one door policy' – social work departments of local authorities should play the lead role in assessing needs, designing care packages and ensuring that they were delivered.

- Local authorities should become enabling bodies with the aim of developing a 'mixed economy of care'. This would provide more consumer choice and improve the quality of service.

- Local authorities should collaborate with health boards, housing departments, voluntary agencies and the private sector to produce 'Community Care Plans'.

- A new system of inspections should be introduced for residential and nursing homes.

- A new funding structure should be introduced for those seeking financial assistance with residential and nursing care.

Health and Social Needs

The biggest difficulty with the new proposals was the distinction between health needs and social needs. Although the local authorities were to be the lead agency in 'Community Care', health needs would still be met by GPs and hospitals, while care needs would still be met by local authorities. So, when a person was discharged from hospital, he or she would cease to be a health problem but would instead become a care problem and the responsibility of a different agency. This has continued to be one of the biggest challenges facing 'Community Care'.

When the new arrangements came into practice in 1990, responses were mixed. Studies suggested that few NHS or local authority workers in Scotland were wholly behind the new proposals. This was hardly surprising given that the idea of 'Community Care' was so heavily influenced by Conservative ideology and that the Conservative Party enjoyed so little support in Scotland.

Within the NHS, workers were most concerned about the introduction of an 'internal market' in health care, including 'Community Care'. Local authorities were pre-occupied with their lead role in assessing needs and care-management. Care-management was the organisation of the process of providing a care package that met the needs of each individual. Progress towards achieving the aims of 'Community Care' has been slower in Scotland than in the rest of the UK.

Local authorities now received the funding which the Department of Social Security had previously provided for paying for places in 'residential care'. They also used part of the 'Revenue Support Grant', the contribution of central government to local government costs, to finance 'Community Care'. Health authorities 'ring-fenced' part of their funding to pay for their share of 'Community Care'.

NHS Provision of Geriatric Long-Stay Beds (1980-1997)

	1980	1991	1993	1995	1997
Number of geriatric long-stay beds	7,196	8,727	7,853	6,790	5,452
Number of geriatric long-stay beds per 1000 people aged 65+	8.8	11.4	10.2	8.7	7.0

Source: Adapted from Community Care, Scotland 1997

How Successful Has Community Care Been?

In assessing the success of the implementation of 'Community Care', three main areas can be examined. These are the balance between institutional and 'Community Care'; the development of a more 'mixed economy of health care' and the level of collaboration between local authority social work departments and health providers.

Institutional and Community Care

Patterns of residential provision for the elderly have changed since the introduction of 'Community Care'. The number of long-stay NHS hospital beds for elderly patients peaked at around 8700 in 1991 and subsequently decreased to around 5000 in 1997. This decrease has to be considered in the context of the increase in numbers of the very old.

However, so-called assessment beds showed an increase by around 37% since 1990, to a figure of 3000. These beds are used to assess the needs and health of elderly people prior to a care plan being designed for them. Between 1987 and 1997, there was a dramatic rise in the number of nursing home places from 5000 to almost 23000. The number of beds in 'residential care' homes rose slightly to 24,000 between 1990 and 1997. This clearly goes against the policy of 'Community Care' which should encourage fewer patients in long-term care. Both long-stay hospital beds and nursing homes represent 'institutional care'.

On the other hand, the growth of 'sheltered housing' is an indication of an increase in 'Community Care'. There are now around four times as many 'sheltered housing' units as there were in 1980. The figure had risen to 37,000 in 1997. Additionally, it was thought that there could be another 3000 private sheltered homes, sometimes known as 'granny flats'.

A Mixed Economy of Health Care

The move towards a 'mixed economy' of provision, with local councils, the NHS and the private and voluntary sectors all involved, was to be achieved by creating a 'purchaser-provider' split in 'Community Care'. Local authorities, as the purchasers, would use their 'Community Care' budget to shop around for the most appropriate care provision, taking account of a number of factors including cost. However, the 'mixed economy' of care provision has not fully developed in Scotland. There are a number of reasons for this.

- Firstly, local councils are not keen to purchase, in many cases preferring to provide their own services. This has been particularly true in the case of home help services.

- Secondly, the need to generate 'Community Care Plans', inspect residential homes and co-ordinate work with other agencies has meant that little time or resources have been available to seek out alternative providers.

- Thirdly, in Scotland especially, there have been few private sector companies in the business of care provision.

Voluntary organisations have become involved in 'Community Care' but not on the scale that the Conservative Government would have liked. They tend to be very conscious of their campaigning role and have not seen service provision as a major priority. Furthermore, if voluntary organisations were to enter into contractual arrangements for the provision of services for financial return, it would raise ethical and moral issues for many of those who support the voluntary agencies.

The private sector has been slow to get involved in some aspects of care provision in Scotland. One reason for this is that they face comparative financial disadvantage in providing services. Local authority services are VAT exempt, whereas private companies are liable for the tax. One area in which private companies are starting to expand is the provision of home nursing. Private companies which provide trained nursing staff to look after people at home, or untrained respite workers to relieve family carers, look likely to expand further in the future.

It is clear that the 'residential care' mix varies considerably by client group. For the frail elderly, local authority and voluntary sector provision has declined while private sector provision has risen. For the mentally ill, local authority provision has all but disappeared, with a huge rise in the voluntary sector. The voluntary sector now provides the majority of care for people with learning difficulties, as opposed to local authorities which dominated this area in the 1980s. The physically disabled have always been cared for predominantly by the voluntary sector.

Collaboration and Co-ordination

The improvement in collaboration and co-ordination between different agencies has not happened on the scale that was anticipated.

The day-to-day demands of providing services have meant that time and resources have been scarce and the expansion of the elderly population has dominated the priorities of the care sector. The Conservative Government hoped that 'GP Fundholding' practices might employ practice care managers – qualified social workers who would consider the care needs of patients on the practice list. Very few practices have considered this option to be viable.

An overall assessment of the progress of 'Community Care' is difficult. The policy has worked for some patients and not for others. In some areas, it has been adopted and applied more widely than others.

Assessment of Community Care Needs

The NHS and Community Care Act (1990) states that local authorities should carry out an assessment of a patient's needs and then decide whether 'Community Care' services should be provided. Sometimes, a specific health problem arises which means that an elderly person has to be admitted to hospital for immediate assessment. Where this has happened, 96% of elderly people have been admitted to hospital for assessment within seven days.

Assessment usually involves establishing various facts about the individual concerned. The individual is given the opportunity to state their own views about their needs and how they should be met. Their needs are then assessed by looking at the following aspects of their life:

Self-Care

What is the person capable of doing for themselves? Can they cook, wash and dress themselves?

Physical Health

The GP will carry out a full medical examination. This will determine what medical support, including medication, is required.

Mental Health

A health professional, usually the community psychiatrist, will carry out an assessment. The mental health of an individual may affect his own perception of his needs.

Use of Medicines

Is the person able to administer their own medicines safely?

Abilities, Attitudes and Lifestyle

Assessment must take account of individual circumstances. Some people have family and friends on whom they can rely; others have nobody. Some people have effectively disengaged from society and take no part in activities and seldom go out or meet anyone. Other elderly people live a very active life.

Personal History

Factors such as the death of a partner should be taken into account. Past involvement with health and social services will also be considered.

Needs of Carers

Informal carers, such as family, must be consulted. They also have needs. Caring for an elderly person should not be an unreasonable burden.

Financial Assessment

This considers the person's home and savings in order to see how much, if anything, they have to pay for services. Of all the residents in Scotland's registered residential care homes, 42% were funded by arrangements with local authorities, 33% were funded privately, 24% wholly or mainly by the DSS and the remainder were funded by health boards. The average weekly charge for residents in homes for older people was £317 for local authority homes, £267 for voluntary homes and £249 for private homes.

Registered Residential Care Homes in Scotland – Funding Arrangements

42% were funded by local authorities
33% were funded privately
24% wholly or mainly by the DSS
1% were funded by health boards
Average weekly charge for residents in homes for older people was £317 for local authority homes, £267 for voluntary homes and £249 for private homes.

The Individual Care Plan

After the initial assessment of an elderly person has taken place, there are three stages to the 'Personal Care Plan'.

- Implementing the care plan means meeting the needs of the individual. Ideally, this should involve as few agencies as possible so as not to confuse the individual concerned. Sometimes, this may involve a care co-ordinator visiting an elderly person.

- Monitoring takes place to see whether the aims are being met over a period of time. The plan may have to be changed if the circumstances of the individual change.

- Reviewing is simply the formal alteration to the plan in the light of changes identified during the monitoring stage.

Recommendations of a Care Co-ordinator

Urgent chiropody
Initial provision of equipment including a commode for use downstairs, a Zimmer frame, raised toilet seat and bed cradle
Referral to district nurse for reassessment of varicose ulcers
Attendance at local day centre once a week to improve confidence about going out for attendance allowance
Referral to an optician for eye test
Private purchase of a leg stool
Private laundry and a domestic cleaning service
Support for family carers

Informal Carers

More than 6 million people (1 in 7 of the adult population) in Britain are informal carers who look after the sick, elderly or disabled on a regular basis. Over a quarter of carers carry the burden alone and do so for at least 20 hours per week. One estimate of the value of informal carers suggests that the Government would have to pay out approximately £24 billion per year for equivalent care.

Carers, many of whom are women, devote time and resources to looking after an elderly friend, relative, partner, spouse or neighbour who is ill or disabled. Many carers are also grown-up children looking after an elderly parent or parents. Many carers feel that they are not given the recognition that they deserve. They need help and support in the caring work that they do and they also need a break from their caring duties. This can be provided when the individual being cared for is taken into 'temporary respite care'.

Since 1996, carers have been entitled to an assessment of their own needs. 'Invalid Care Allowance' is available to help with the costs of caring and to compensate for the fact that a full-time carer cannot work. However, the rules for claiming 'Invalid Care Allowance' are strict and the amount paid is not generous. Only 110,000 people, 2% of carers nationally, were eligible for 'Invalid Care Allowance', even after married women became eligible to claim.

The Cost of Care

'Modernising Community Care: An Action Plan' (1998), gave examples of the types of package and costs for different circumstances. 'Community Care' costs compare favourably with the costs for other forms of care. A hospital bed costs £33,000 per year, a nursing home bed costs £16,000 per year and a place in a residential care home costs between £13,000 and £17,000 per year.

Criticisms of Community Care

An Unachievable Ideal?

Almost everyone agrees that trying to meet a person's needs in their own home is the best solution. However, given the resources required and the harsh financial realities of government spending, 'Community Care' may be an unachievable ideal. It may be that 'Community Care' tries to spread resources too thinly amongst too many people with the result that few people have their needs met fully.

One of the assumptions made at the time of the introduction of 'Community Care' was that it would be cheaper than 'residential care'. This is not necessarily the case. Many health and social care experts believe that 'Community Care' works out more expensively than care in a hospital and that additional funding has not been made available to compensate for this. With the increasing numbers of elderly people in the UK, pressure on budgets will grow in the future. This may mean that more money needs to be spent on 'Community Care'. This can only be financed through increased taxation at local or national level or by reducing spending on other areas. It is worth noting that the Scottish Parliament has tax-varying powers and, although promises have been made to the electorate not to use these powers in the short term, it may be that 'Community Care' may become the social and economic issue which ignites this particular political debate.

The Future of Community Care

The new Labour Government, elected in May 1997, produced a White Paper called 'Designed to Care', in which they set out a new vision for the National Health Service in Scotland, based on co-operation rather than competition. Tony Blair, in his preface to the White Paper, said:

"this White Paper marks a turning point for the NHS in Scotland. It replaces the internal market. We are saving £100 million of red tape and putting that money into frontline patient care in Scotland."

'Community Care' will come under a new system of management and it is hoped that a collaborative approach will pay dividends in terms of higher standards of care. Towards the end of 1997, the Government also established a Royal Commission to investigate the funding of long-term care for elderly people.

The Labour Government has re-affirmed a commitment to 'Community Care' as the best way of dealing with the problems of older people. It wishes to emphasise the need to provide co-ordinated, structured care and support for all vulnerable individuals and groups in a manner which responds closely to their assessed needs.

The aim also is to allow those requiring care to remain in their own homes and communities as long as that remains a practical and safe option. Where continuing care in a more structured setting is necessary, the aim is to provide that care and accommodation in the community and in small domestic settings such as 'sheltered housing'.

A set of core standards for nursing homes was published in July 1988. It set out the standards by which all nursing homes in Scotland will be assessed by health boards. Every nursing home will now be subject to at least three inspections per year.

The Future of 'Community Care'

The Labour Government's Priorities

Better and Faster Decision-making

- delegate decision-making and budgets
- streamline management
- transfer of resources to front-line services
- improved partnerships between agencies

Home Care

- care for people at home wherever possible
- develop more flexible home care services
- provide suitable housing
- encourage health and social care services to cooperate

Local Cooperation

- develop integrated services
- plan and deliver services based on the needs of each locality
- encourage new approaches to the way services are managed and delivered, based on local partnerships

Bidding for Resources

- funding based on firm proposals for change
- target resources on authorities who are shifting the balance of care, developing more flexible home care services and working in partnerships

The Politics of Health

Introduction

Given the consensus among the main British and Scottish political parties on the existence of the NHS, the main differences in party policies are quantitative rather than qualitative, differences of degree rather than principle. There will be arguments over the level of funding, how the NHS is organised, pay policy and other more administrative matters but the basic principles of the NHS will not be in dispute.

In a situation like this, where there is not a great deal of ideological difference between the parties, the Government of the day tends to be very proactive, even more so than in other areas of public policy. It will set the agenda, simply because it is the administration in charge of the day-to-day running of the NHS. Consequently, other parties in opposition will react to what the Government does or says. The Government will listen to the other parties, to interest and pressure groups and to others with something to say about health care but it will remain the most important player in this particular game.

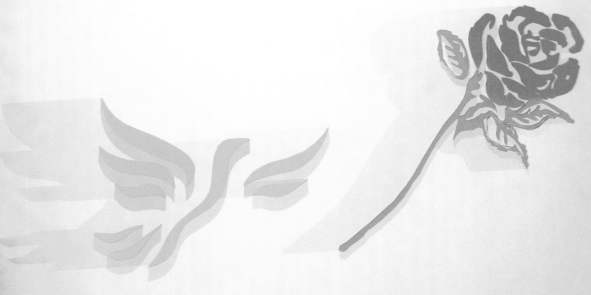

STUDY TOPIC 1

What are the differences in party policies and ideologies?

The 1997 General Election

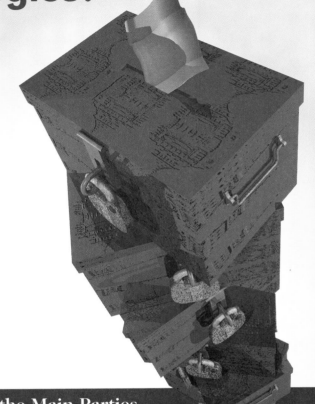

One of the best opportunities for political parties to get their message across is during an election campaign. The 1997 General Election campaign was fought on a range of issues including the fitness, rather than simply the competence, of the Conservatives to govern. The Conservatives, as might be expected, defended their record on the NHS, pointing to the increased spending, more patients being treated than ever before and the benefits of their reforms. The role of the opposition parties, especially the Labour Party, was to point out deficiencies in the Conservative Government's record and to propose their own alternative policies.

Manifesto Commitments on Health of the Main Parties in Scotland for the United Kingdom General Election (1997)

The Conservative Party

- NHS internal market to remain

- 'GP Fundholding' to be developed

- Waiting lists to be cut

- Primary care-led NHS - 'super-surgeries' to be developed to perform minor surgery, extending role of pharmacists, nurses and therapists to perform some tasks previously only done by doctors

- Local authorities to purchase 'residential' and 'Community Care' in the private or voluntary sector unless places are inadequate or dearer than in public sector

- Only elderly and incurable patients who require complex or intensive medical or nursing care to continue to be treated by NHS

- Combination of mental and social services to establish new authority for mental health care

- Continued increase in NHS spending annually by more than rate of inflation

The Labour Party

- Retain 'purchaser/provider' split of 'internal market'
- Replace 'GP Fundholding' with system of GPs jointly commissioning care from hospitals and health authorities on area basis
- Local councillor on boards of hospital trusts
- Waiting lists to be reduced by releasing £100 million saved from cutting bureaucracy
- Conservative proposals to be maintained on primary care
- All tobacco advertising to be banned
- Minister for Public Health to be appointed
- Royal Commission to make recommendations on a fair system of funding long-term care for the elderly to be established
- Closure of psychiatric beds to be halted until appropriate community services are available

The Liberal Democratic Party

- 'Hypothecated' taxation - taxes which would raise money to be spent on specific areas, e.g., an increase on tobacco taxes to increase spending on the NHS
- In Scotland, the internal market to be replaced with a more collaborative approach to providing services
- Overall strategy for health promotion to tackle deprivation and environmental causes of ill-health
- Greater emphasis on health education

The Scottish National Party

- The 'internal market' to be abolished
- Spending in Scotland to be increased by £35 million per annum
- Dentistry to be reintegrated into the NHS
- Prescription charge levels and exemptions to be reviewed
- Cigarette advertising to be banned
- Preventive medicine to be promoted
- Resources for 'Community Care' to be increased

The Labour Government and the NHS

The newly elected Labour Government's plans for the NHS were published in White Papers in December 1997 – 'The New NHS' (England) and 'Designed to Care' (Scotland).

The underlying principles of the White Papers were to:

Renew the NHS as a genuinely national service

■ Patients to get fair access to consistently high quality, prompt and accessible services right across the country.

Shift the focus on to quality of care

■ Excellence to be guaranteed to all patients and quality to become the driving force for decision-making at every level of the service.

Rebuild public confidence in the NHS

■ A public service accountable to patients, open to the public and shaped by their views.

Get the NHS to work in partnership

■ Break down organisational barriers, forge links with local authorities and patient needs to be put at the centre of the care process.

Make the delivery of health care a matter of local responsibility

■ Local doctors and nurses to be regarded as being in the best position to know what patients need and to be at forefront of shaping new services.

Drive efficiency and cut bureaucracy

■ Every £1 spent on the NHS to be spent maximising patient care.

A Modern and Dependable NHS

The aim of the White Papers was to create a modern and dependable NHS by providing new and better services, not just in hospitals, but in communities and in the home. In hospital, patients would receive prompt access to specialist services, so that, e.g., anyone with suspected cancer would be seen urgently. In the community, people would be given swift advice and treatment in local surgeries and health centres, with family doctors and community nurses working alongside other health and social care staff to provide a wide range of services on the spot. At home, there would be easier and faster access to advice and information through a new 24-hour advice line staffed by nurses.

Designed to Care

The Labour Party was opposed to the 'internal market' in the NHS while it was in opposition. In government, it has set about delivering its manifesto commitment to abolish these arrangements. However, the Government has stated that it does not want to return to the old system of what it calls "command and control" from the centre, with little scope for local initiatives or local decision-making.

The emphasis is to be on collaboration and planning through local 'Health Improve-ment Programmes' (HIPs) agreed by health boards, NHS Trusts and general practitioners.

HIPs are to be open to public scrutiny, including the Local Health Council (a body with representatives of NHS users including local community groups). Each HIP is to cover a period of five years and has to set out:

- Proposals to protect public health including emergency planning.
- Proposals to promote health.
- Proposals to analyse and tackle health inequalities.
- Service changes and developments, including those involving primary care.
- A rolling programme for the implementation of evidence-based clinical guidelines and clinically effective practice to be monitored through clinical audit.

The Government's plans to abolish the 'internal market' include redefined responsibilities and administrative roles for each part of the NHS.

Health Boards

Health boards have the lead role in developing HIPs and will retain their existing responsibilities in relation to public health protection, health improvements, needs assessment, service strategy and performance management and will be given a small number of new powers to ensure that local strategies can be implemented, e.g., to ensure that Trusts are being held properly to account. Boards will also have to work closely with local authorities to deliver these responsibilities.

NHS Trusts

Trusts are retained and refocussed on improving the quality of service to patients by giving medical and nursing staff who work in hospitals and those who use their services a bigger say in their management.

The number of Trusts has been reduced from 46 to 28. The Government say this will save £18 million which will go directly to patient care. There are now two main types of trust:

- Acute Trusts comprise all acute hospitals within a health board area although in Greater Glasgow and Lothian there is more than one Acute Trust. (Because of special local circumstances, the Island Health Boards of Orkney, Shetland and the Western Isles continue to manage their hospitals directly.) Each will have a budget allocated to it by its health board. The Government published an 'Acute Services Review' in 1998. This took account of its reforms and of other changing circumstances to plan the provision of these services at a national level for the following ten years.

- Primary Care Trusts (PCTs) comprise of general practitioners, community nurses, midwives and therapists. Each PCT will have a budget allocated to it by its health board. GPs are grouped together in Local Health Care Cooperatives which, if they wish, can have their own budgets for primary and community health services. As well as delivering integrated primary services, PCTs have to work with boards and Acute Trusts to develop the HIP for their area and to agree the design and delivery of clinical services around the needs of their patients, including what can be delivered at primary level and what is best done by hospitals.

Joint Investment Funds

Joint Investment Funds are set up by health boards to finance any changes which may be necessary to implement these plans for the delivery of clinical services.

It can be observed that the approach of the Labour Government to the delivery of the NHS is different to that of the previous Conservative administration, in that the Labour Government's emphasis is on collaboration and planning to deliver efficiently what is necessary to patients. Its predecessor felt that the discipline of competition in the market place was the best way. This is one example of how the basic ideologies of the main parties differ and how these can affect the practical implementation of their policies.

Delivering an Efficient NHS – Two Options
Labour Government Policy - collaboration and planning
Conservative Party Policy - competition in the market place

Working Together for a Healthier Scotland

The Conservative Government did not acknowledge the need for action in this area. The relationship between poverty and ill-health was seen as a problem of lack of health education among some social classes rather than a broader social and economic issue. The newly elected Labour Government took a different approach. In 1998, it published 'Deprivation and Health in Scotland', using official NHS data to demonstrate the link between poverty and ill-health. This publication was given prominence in Government media briefings and the fact that it took place at all is a reflection of the differing attitudes of the Labour and Conservative Governments to the problem.

Earlier in the same year, the Government signalled its intention to tackle inequalities in health by publishing a Green Paper (for consultation) – 'Working Together for a Healthier Scotland'. A separate Green Paper, 'Our Healthier Nation', was published in England.

When a government acknowledges that the problems of health inequalities arise from general social and economic conditions then solutions have to be more than medical and must involve other areas. Thus, in addition to the NHS, the Government acknowledged the input necessary from local authorities, voluntary organisations and the private sector.

THE SCOTTISH OFFICE

ISBN 0 10 142692 5

Publisher The Stationery Office.   Price £6.00
1999

Towards a Healthier Scotland - A White Paper on Health

Presented to Parliament by the Secretary of State for Scotland
by Command of Her Majesty
February 1999

Cm 4269

NEMO ME IMPUNE LACESSIT

Contents
Foreword
Summary
Chapter 1 Setting the Scene
Chapter 2 A Shared Vision for Action
Chapter 3 Action: Life Circumstances
Chapter 4 Action: Lifestyles
Chapter 5 Action: Health Topics
Chapter 6 Putting the Jigsaw Together
Chapter 7 Health Demonstration Projects
Chapter 8 Research, Evaluation, Targets and Monitoring
Chapter 9 Conclusion
Appendix 1 Action List
References

The information contained on this WWW site is Crown Copyright but may be reproduced without formal permission or charge for personal or in-house use.
© 1999

Working Together for a Healthier Scotland

- Health Impact Assessments to be carried out by Central Government before any new policies are introduced.

- Local communities to be involved in planning of new initiatives in their area and in identifying existing initiatives as examples of good practice.

- Implementation and extension of Central Government policies such as the New Deal for the unemployed and the introduction of a National Minimum Wage.

- Action to improve the environment by tackling poor housing and related problems, e.g., homelessness.

- Extension of existing health board involvement in area regeneration programmes which tackle multiple deprivation in inner city and other run-down areas.

- The Scottish Prison Service to examine how health can be improved in prisons, e.g., through tackling drug misuse.

- The establishment of a network of Healthy Living Centres in deprived communities to target smoking, poor diet, lack of exercise and alcohol and drug abuse.

- Development of new initiatives to tackle the lifestyle problems of smoking, alcohol and drug misuse, poor diet and lack of exercise.

- Public debate and consultation on fluoridisation of water supply and on how to reduce teenage pregnancies.

- Development and implementation of local strategies for mental health in collaboration with social work, housing and other agencies.

- Campaign against and advice to victims of domestic violence.

- Increased funding for the prevention of communicable diseases, including HIV infection and E-coli.

- Funding for a public health post in COSLA (the Convention of Scottish Local Authorities) to draw up good practice guidance and other advice on health improvement for councils.

- Health Education Board for Scotland (HEBS) to implement its Strategic Plan for 1997-2000, with emphasis on the 'Big Three' of cancer, heart disease and strokes.

- Specialist unit to be established by HEBS to further develop health education in schools.

- Encouragement to industry and commerce to contribute to good health.

- Encouragement to the voluntary sector to continue its contribution to promoting good health.

Waiting Lists

One of the key promises which Labour made in its manifesto was to cut hospital waiting lists by 100,000 in the lifetime of a parliament, i.e., in five years. However, at the the end of its first year in power, waiting lists had actually grown.

This was partly a result of extra resources being used in the winter months to ensure that there were adequate Accident and Emergency facilities to cope with casualties of bad weather. Waiting lists began to even out by the end of 1998 and, in Scotland, were falling in 1999.

However, many critics regarded this relative success as being due to the converse of the reason for the rise the previous year – that resources were being diverted from other priorities, such as Accident and Emergency, to be used to cut lists. They cited the crisis in Accident and Emergency units in many parts of the country in the winter of 1998-99 as evidence of this.

Government critics had two main arguments:

■ Political opponents argued that the increases in expenditure which the Government had announced were not enough.

■ Critics within the medical and nursing professions argued that, although the extra resources were welcome, it was too simple to regard the length of waiting lists as the one criterion by which to judge the well-being of the health service – other areas were being neglected to allow the Government to meet its manifesto commitment.

Private Finance Initiative

PFIs were introduced by the Conservative Government. The intention was to allow public service providers, such as the NHS, to find sources of finance for capital projects which did not have to draw on the public purse. It could work, for example, by a 'Public-Private Partnership', whereby a hospital would be built and owned by a private company, while the NHS would lease the building, effectively a tenant of the private landlord. The NHS would pay for the lease but the building would remain the property of the private company.

The advantage of this is that such projects do not have to compete with others to be financed by public expenditure, allowing the Government to undertake capital projects while not affecting public borrowing. Lower public borrowing would allow the Government to keep its options open on joining the 'Single European Currency', which requires that, before entry, countries have low levels of government borrowing.

Such schemes are in their infancy and it may be some years before a proper evaluation as to whether the benefits claimed for them or the criticisms made against them are accurate.

Community Care

In 1998, the Labour Government announced that it was to end the element of 'Community Care' which applied to psychiatric patients (at least in England). It argued that the previous policy had let down both the patient and the public. It had been estimated that one killing every two weeks had been committed by patients released into the community. There were to be tough and effective policies to ensure that this did not occur. The focus would be on 24-hour care, based on new specialist support units and outreach teams who will keep track of patients.

Other Initiatives by the Labour Government

NHS Direct
A telephone hotline, staffed by qualified nurses to allow the public 24-hour access to the NHS to answer queries. This will be extended to Scotland in 2000.

Health Action Zones
Collaboration by Health Boards, GPs and local authorities to tackle poor health.

Eyesight Tests
Restoration of free eyesight tests for the elderly.

Prescription Fraud
A crack down on prescription fraud said to cost the NHS an estimated £30 million per annum.

Food Standards Agency
A Food Standards Agency to be set up to look at every step in food production to protect public health by ensuring that the public are not harmed by the food they eat.

One Stop Clinics
One stop clinics to provide tests, results and diagnosis on the same day.

Electronic Links
Patients to know the date of their hospital appointments before they leave their GP's surgery through the use of electronic links between hospitals and GPs' surgeries.

Scottish Health Technology Assessment Centre
A Scottish Health Technology Assessment Centre to provide guidance on the introduction of new medical technologies including drugs.

Removal of Tax Relief
The removal of tax relief for the elderly on 'private medical insurance' to finance a cut in VAT from 8% to 5% on domestic fuel.

Quality Assurance
A nationally organised process of quality assurance for clinical services.

Ban on Tobacco Advertising and Sponsorship
The eventual ban of all tobacco advertising and sponsorship by 2005.

STUDY TOPIC 2

In what ways do governments and opposition parties influence the provision and consumption of health care?

Influencing the Provision and Consumption of Health Care

The Government is proactive in health policy while the other political parties have to react to the actions and statements of the Government and attempt to influence the provision and consumption of health care. The Labour Government came to power in May 1997 and, in eighteen months, had begun all the initiatives described above. Some commentators have suggested that, by any definition, the Labour Government "hit the ground running" in relation to health care.

Other parties, having just fought a General Election, with carefully thought-out policies, had to respond almost piecemeal to all these initiatives and, at the same time, give some thought to defining alternatives. This is a process which can sometimes take the length of a parliament. The parties in Scotland, Wales and Northern Ireland, however, had to develop policies to fight elections in 1999 to the Scottish Parliament and the Assemblies in Wales and Northern Ireland. These give a clear indication to the thinking of the other parties on health although there were some policy statements made by the other parties even before then.

The Conservative Party

As the Official Opposition, the Conservatives have a constitutional duty to seek out and publicise any inadequacies or even follies which they perceive in the way the Government is performing. Three areas in particular were highlighted by the Conservatives.

Bed-Blocking

Bed-blocking is the term used to describe the situation where hospital beds cannot be freed for use because they are occupied by elderly people, who have finished their course of medical care, but are either too frail to be discharged into their own homes or there is no proper alternative accommodation into which they can be discharged. Elderly people want to be treated in their own homes and most of them could be if the necessary nursing and social support were available. The Conservatives argued that the Government's financial settlement for local authorities was making this difficult to achieve. The Conservatives recommended that there should be more imaginative schemes to prevent elderly people being admitted inappropriately to hospital in the first place - an experience which can have a long-term damaging effect on an elderly person's ability to maintain independence.

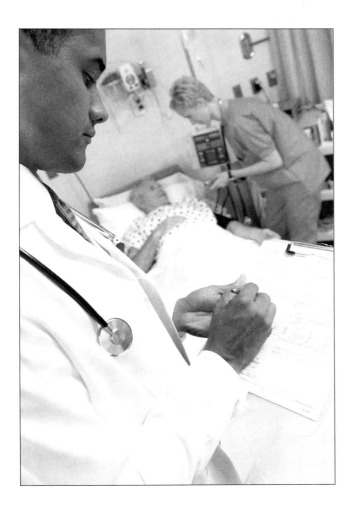

Phantom Health Initiatives

In 1998, the Conservatives launched a campaign against what they called 'phantom health initiatives'. They asked professionals working in the NHS to alert them to any new schemes announced by the Government which health boards were unable to put into practice because insufficient funds were available.

Broken Promises

The Conservatives announced their intention to publicise what they said were broken promises.on the NHS by the Government. One announcement which gained headlines throughout the country was the announcement of 13 cuts in services or closures of units in hospitals across London. They cited pledges by Labour spokespersons before the election that there would be no such cuts nor closures as evidence of broken government promises.

The Liberal Democratic Party

As a smaller party, the Liberal Democrats do not have the same resources nor are guaranteed the same access to the media to publicise their statements and campaigns. However, they do have a similar role to that of the Official Opposition, in that they will criticise the shortcomings, as they perceive them, of the Government and offer alternative proposals. Their plans included proposals to:

- spend an extra £550 million on the NHS, financed by extra taxes on tobacco products and by closing loopholes in employers' National Insurance Contributions;
- ban all tobacco advertising and sponsorship of sports and arts events;
- reintroduce free eyesight tests for all;
- introduce rights for carers.
- postpone any closures in the NHS for six months;
- establish one national pay body for all NHS workers;
- compensate the NHS for the use by the private sector of doctors, nurses and other staff trained by the NHS;
- review all existing 'Public-Private Partnerships' under the 'Private Finance Initiative'.

The Liberal Democrats also demanded that the Government take emergency action to help the NHS function properly during its first winter in office. Again, it showed how it regarded extra funding, over and above any that the Government had announced, as the only solution – in this instance, £150 million to cut waiting lists and £200 million to improve pay and conditions and recruit new staff.

The Liberal Democrats also called for an increase in the number of medical students and the necessary public funding to pay for them, using statistics to show that a doctor shortage was developing in the medium term. The Party criticised the Government for phasing, i.e., not paying the nurses' pay award in full in one instalment and for raising prescription charges to £5.80 per item in 1998.

The Scottish National Party

More than the other United Kingdom parties, the Scottish National Party regarded its proposals for the Scottish Parliament as being of great importance. Between the 1997 Westminster General Election and the first elections for the Scottish Parliament in 1999, it made a number of policy statements on health care in Scotland.

The Scottish National Party

The abolition of the internal market

■ A reduced emphasis to be placed on market forces.

The establishment of an independent Health Commission

■ Chaired by the Health Minister, with representatives of all political parties and health professionals, to plan the strategic delivery of health services.

Local Health Commissions

■ To undertake the planning to deliver health services locally.

The reintegration of dentistry into the NHS

■ Greater rewards for dentists to encourage an attack on Scotland's poor dental record compared to other parts of the UK.

An alternative to the Private Finance Initiative

■ A Scottish Public Services Trust, with a board of directors chosen from all parties in the new Scottish Parliament and representatives from the Convention of Scottish Local Authorities (COSLA). It would be charged with seeking capital from financial institutions at advantageous interest rates and with issuing guaranteed interest-bearing bonds to fund new hospitals, as well as schools and other public works.

The Scottish Parliament

From 1st July, 1999, the NHS in Scotland became the responsibility of the Scottish Executive, accountable to the Scottish Parliament. In February 1999, the Scottish Office had published a White Paper, 'Towards a Healthier Scotland', based on the results of the consultations following the Green Paper 'Working Together for a Healthier Scotland'. The Government defined the overarching aim of its White Paper as "tackling inequalities".

Since the White Paper was published by a Westminster Labour Government, it could be assumed that a Labour Government in the Scottish Parliament would continue with the intentions outlined in the White Paper. If a government emerged from the Scottish Parliament which did not include Labour, that Government would have to take positive action to put a halt to any of these intentions with which it disagreed.

Tackling Inequalities – Three Action Levels for Better Health

Life Circumstances

- A sustained programme of social and economic change supported by new funding.

- The Scottish Office to ensure that its economic and social policies have a positive health impact in the drive to tackle inequality, improve educational participation and attainment, boost housing and employment and promote 'social inclusion'.

- All Scotland's local councils to be asked to make health improvement a corporate goal and, using community planning, to improve the circumstances in which people live.

- The Scottish Office and the Health Education Board for Scotland (HEBS) to work, in partnership, with health boards, the Convention of Scottish Local Authorities (COSLA), local councils, the voluntary sector, mass media and other interests to stimulate a 'pro health' culture.

Tackling Inequalities – Three Action Levels for Better Health

Lifestyles

Smoking

- New laws to ban tobacco advertising.
- Enhanced health promotion campaigns, targeting young people, pregnant women and low income smokers.
- New NHS services to help smokers quit.
- Improved facilities in pubs and restaurants for non-smokers.
- Consultation on a better way to reduce 'passive smoking' at work.
- Tougher enforcement of the law against sales of tobacco to children.

Diet

- Increased funding for Scottish Diet Action Plan initiatives.
- A new Food Standards Agency to improve access by people to information about nutrition and food safety.

Physical Activity

- A National Physical Activity Strategy for Scotland to be developed to bring together key agencies in sport and leisure, education, health, fitness, exercise and play, in joint action to help people of all ages and walks of life to enjoy the benefits of physical activity.

Alcohol Misuse

- New steps to cut alcohol misuse.
- A new strategy bringing together experts from the health service, police, local authorities, licensing authorities and the voluntary and private sectors.

Drug Misuse

- The Government to co-ordinate and focus drug misuse measures in Scotland.
- New prevention and treatment services to discourage drug misuse, offer effective treatment and cut drug-linked crime.

Tackling Inequalities – Three Action Levels for Better Health

Health Topics

- The Government to support children and their families in fulfilling their potential and to support children's health from pre-conception through to school entry.

- The Government to fund pilot schemes to provide fluoridated milk in rural areas where fluoridation of the public water supply is not feasible.

- The Government to commission, and fund, the development of a dental disease 'prevention from birth' programme, involving registration with a dentist, dental education for all new parents, toothbrushing with a fluoride toothpaste for infants and advice on how to reduce sugar in the diet of infants.

- The development of best practice in the promotion of sexual health and the prevention of unwanted teenage pregnancies.

- Heart disease to be a leading priority for the NHS in Scotland. A national media campaign to address the factors which contribute to coronary heart disease as one of Scotland's main killing diseases. Accelerated action on smoking and diet to help drive down rates of heart disease.

- Cancer to be a leading priority for the NHS in Scotland. Linking with its work on coronary heart disease and strokes, HEBS to increase its national media activity to promote awareness of the factors which help to make cancer one of Scotland's main killing diseases. Accelerated action on smoking and diet to help drive down cancer rates.

- Mental health to be a leading priority for the NHS in Scotland. 'Social inclusion' initiatives to help improve well-being and so enhance mental health.

Manifesto Commitments on Health of the Main Parties in Scotland for the Scottish Parliamentary Elections (1999)

The Labour Party

Improve services to patients

- Involve patients more in decisions about their care and treatment
- Provide patients with more information about their health and options for treatment
- Use new technology to speed treatment and shorten waiting lists
- Set and enforce new standards of care for all hospitals

Deliver excellence in health

- Build eight new hospital developments
- Reduce waiting lists by at least 10,000 from the 1997 level and then reduce them further through targeting areas with longest lists
- Introduce 'airline booking' systems, so that people know the time of their hospital appointment before they leave their GP's surgery
- Introduce a 'walk in / walk out' hospital service to provide same day treatment from specialist staff
- Reduce waiting times for seeing a consultant
- Double the number of one-stop clinics
- Increase (by at least 500) the number of coronary by-pass operations
- Develop a network of Healthy Living Centres
- Create a new centre of excellence in rural health care in Inverness

Aim to achieve the following targets by 2010

- Halve deaths from coronary heart disease
- Cut deaths from cancer by 20%
- Cut smoking among young people by 20%

The Scottish National Party

The future of the NHS

- A period of non-disruption for the Scottish Health Service
- Establish a National Health Care Commission, chaired by the Minister of Health with cross party representation of MSPs, representatives of the health profession and unions together with members of the wider community to have responsibility for planning the future strategy of health care in Scotland

Improve public health

- Create a Minister of Public Health to oversee not just Public Health, but the Party's anti-poverty programme

Primary health care

- Local health care cooperatives to be encouraged to construct a code of best practice regarding the organisation and function of primary care teams to ensure that some services, e.g., chemotherapy for cancer patients, are brought closer to the community and, where possible, made available at community clinics, GPs' surgeries or even the home
- Access to GP health care to be guaranteed, with GPs obliged to state in writing why they wish to remove a person from their list, and with a right of appeal for the patient.
- Promote the use of information technology to provide expert care to remote communities

Improve 'Community Care'

- Introduce a national framework for standards in 'Community Care'
- Involve mental health organisations in the proposed National Health Care Commission and develop a national strategy

Capital investment

- Introduce Scottish Public Service Trusts to oversee investment in the public sector for the building of new hospitals.

The Liberal Democratic Party

Improve public health
- Priority to promoting public health
- Improve damp and cold housing
- Reduce alcohol, tobacco and drug abuse
- Improve nutritional standards
- Abolish charges for eye and dental checks
- Support initiatives in the public, private and voluntary sectors and give local councils more responsibilities for public health and health promotion

Boost the NHS
- Increase resources and make real improvements in the NHS
- Establish maximum waiting times in every specialty
- Reward NHS staff properly - support the principle of common pay and conditions across the UK for NHS staff
- Give nurses more flexible hours, ensure that agreements to limit junior hospital doctors' hours are adhered to, improve staff training
- Employ more doctors and more nurses, encourage former nurses to return, tackle the shortages in professions like chiropody and speech therapy

Streamline the NHS
- End the division between the health and social services budgets, transferring resources to residential homes, to free up hospital beds for those who really need them
- Establish a new Ministry of Health and Social Services
- Establish a Scottish Standing Commission on Health to advise on NHS strategy and establish priorities based on clinical need, higher standards and length of waiting times

- Ensure proper scrutiny of appointments to NHS Trust boards
- All health board and trust meetings to be open to the public
- Link all health buildings to NHS Net within five years to give doctors faster access to patients' records and allow long distance consultation with consultants
- Build new health facilities where required

Develop 'Community Care'
- Establish a new independent Scottish Inspectorate to monitor and publish standards for residential and nursing homes
- Review charges for social and long-term care; argue for a higher threshold at which older people have to contribute to their own care
- Provide simpler arrangements for financial management for incapable adults
- Improve provision for mental health patients; establish 24 hour mental health centres
- Establish a common way forward in achieving the recommendations contained in the Royal Commission on Long Term Care

Establish Community Partnership Trusts
- Replace Private Finance Initiative agreements
- Alter current rules regarding investment so that the public retain the right to own the assets at the end of the contract period

The Conservative Party

Ensure a fair deal for NHS staff

- Set up a clinician-led working party to examine morale and working issues
- Create more NHS creches and pre-five education for children of NHS staff
- Introduce 'modern matrons' to provide a visible leader on each ward

Work towards less bureaucracy

- Abolish health boards, Primary Care Trusts and GP Cooperatives
- Instruct the Minister for Health and a Parliamentary Standing Committee (with administration of the NHS carried out by the Common Services Agency) to plan services and allocate resources, currently done by boards

Provide better local health care

- Use telemedicine to allow access to centres of excellence for people in remote areas
- Allocate budgets to GPs on the basis of number of patients on their lists, with adjustments to take account of differing local needs
- Invest money saved from cuts in bureaucracy in improving local health care and modernising hospitals
- Build more local community hospitals where patients would go to, after surgery in large hospitals, thus freeing beds in the latter

Strive for excellence in hospitals

- Give more say to professionals in management of hospitals, with greater representation of doctors on NHS Trust boards

Improve public health

- Require HEBS to work in conjunction with Community Health Trusts, local surgeries, clusters of schools and local authority leisure facilities on innovative local schemes to improve health
- Develop national targets to improve treatment of chronic heart disease, cancer, strokes and mental illness

Develop 'Community Care'

- Create a 'real partnership' between public and private sectors in the provision of 'residential' and 'nursing care'
- Set up Community Health Trusts to administer 'Community Care', drawing in NHS primary care, social services, voluntary organisations and churches

The Partnership for Scotland

The first elections for the new Scottish Parliament resulted in no party having an overall majority. The largest party, Labour, and the Liberal Democrats agreed to form a coalition government and to implement a programme called the 'Partnership for Scotland' for the various areas of responsibility of the Parliament. The new Scottish First Minister, Donald Dewar appointed Susan Deacon, Labour MSP for East Edinburgh and Musselburgh, to be Minister for Health and Community Care. The 'Partnership for Scotland' document states that:

Principles

- We believe that high quality health care is the right of all.
- We will promote better health for all across every department of the Scottish Government, tackle the root causes of ill health and create an NHS which puts patients first.
- We will implement distinctive solutions to the health problems of Scotland.
- Our aim is to create the most modern health service in Europe.

Initiatives

- We will make promoting public health a priority for the Minister responsible for health matters.
- We will establish a team cutting across relevant departments to ensure that the public health agenda is delivered in an integrated and effective way.
- We will build a Health Promotion Fund to support health initiatives in the public, private and voluntary sectors.

Initiatives (continued)

- We will halve deaths from coronary heart disease, cut deaths from cancer by 20% and cut smoking among young people.
- We will improve cold and damp housing to promote better health.
- We will create a network of Healthy Living Centres.
- We will support the new Food Standards Agency and its Scottish Advisory Committee.
- We will appoint a Minister of Health and Social Work in order to promote joint working and effective co-operation between health and social work and their budgets.
- We will provide patient-centred care throughout Scotland by:
  - establishing new One Stop Clinics to provide same day tests and diagnosis;
  - providing 24-hour access to health advice through NHS Direct;
  - launching NHS Net to link doctors' surgeries, hospitals and pharmacies electronically;
  - creating walk-in/walk-out centres to offer same day treatment by specialist staff.
- We will increase the information available to NHS patients, particularly on discharge from hospital.
- We will set and monitor targets to speed treatment and shorten waiting times.
- We will seek the guidance of the Parliamentary Health Committee on NHS strategy and priorities.
- We will establish an independent Scottish Inspectorate of Health and Social Care.
- We will substantially increase NHS spending in real terms over the coming years.
- We will increase the numbers of doctors and recruit more nurses and will introduce family friendly policies to encourage the return of trained nurses to the profession.
- We are committed to the biggest hospital building programme in Scotland's history to raise the standards of health care.
- We will expand treatment and rehabilitation facilities for drug, alcohol and substance abusers.
- We accept that 'Public-Private Partnerships' will continue to be one of the ways used to increase innovation and investment in public services where this approach represents best value.
- We will continue to work to improve the operation of public/private partnerships, and will seek opportunities for new types of partnership and flexible contracts which will allow assets, when appropriate, to revert to public ownership.

Priority

- Our priority will be delivering high quality public services while protecting the interests of the community.

STUDY TOPIC 3

How do differing interest and pressure groups influence policy within the field of health care?

Government, Party Politics and Pressure Groups

The National Health Service (NHS) is a term which is so familiar that its significance can be easily forgotten. It is a national service in that it is provided by the Government. In a democratic society, it is provided by the Government on behalf of the people to meet their health needs.

The Government must secure the will of the people in an election to implement its policies to deliver the NHS. It is accountable in subsequent elections to the people for its delivery of the NHS. The Government has to find resources to deliver the NHS and to gain the approval of the people's representatives in Parliament each year to raise and spend the necessary funds.

It could be argued also that, in a democratic society, approval of any proposals to increase or decrease significantly these resources or to make significant changes in the way the service is delivered should be sought from the people in a prior election. This raises the question as to how political parties seeking power can balance the desire of the people for greater spending on the NHS with the equally strong desire of the people not to pay too high taxes – desires both of which most practical politicians recognise as being real, but also conflicting.

The NHS – Beyond Political Debate?

All the main political parties now place great importance on the NHS as a political issue and their election manifestos reflect this, as does the quantity (if not quality) of debate on the NHS between the parties during and between election campaigns.

There are also many pressure and interest groups which relate to the NHS, ranging from trade unions and professional associations, which promote policies for the NHS, as well as attempting to protect the interests of their members, to charities with specific areas of interest over which they try to exercise influence.

At its outset in 1948, the NHS was a political issue which divided the two main parties. The post-war Labour Government's proposals met opposition from the Conservative Party, even though these were based on a consensus of all parties in the wartime coalition government. Significantly, the NHS was also opposed originally by the British Medical Association (BMA), which represents doctors. Nowadays, all the main British and Scottish political parties support the NHS as does the BMA and other NHS trade unions and professional associations.

Differences between the parties nowadays relate more to the administration of the NHS and to different emphases on aspects of health care, rather than to ideological or qualitative differences over whether the NHS should exist in the first place. That the NHS is supported by all the main parties and survived even the ideological upheaval of the 'Thatcher revolution' of the 1980s is an indication of how highly it is regarded by the British people and how it is viewed by the main parties as a national institution whose existence is beyond political debate.

Pressure Groups and the NHS

Trade Unions

The NHS is a concentration of economic activity as well as being a public service. It is a major employer with many workers who have trade unions and professional associations to protect their interests and to propose policies for the NHS as a whole.

The largest trade union in the NHS is UNISON which was formed by the amalgamation of three former trade unions – the National Union of Public Employees (NUPE), the Confederation of Health Service Employees (COHSE) and the National and Local Government Officers' Association (NALGO). Members of UNISON work in the NHS in various capacities including nurses, clerical and administrative staff and ancillary workers. Many nurses belong also to the Royal College of Nursing (RCN), a professional association dedicated solely to the interests of nurses.

Seeking Improvements in Pay and Conditions

The main activity of trade unions is in the area of pay and conditions. The pay and conditions of nurses are determined by a 'review body' and not through normal 'collective bargaining'. This does not mean, however, that UNISON has no role to play. It will consult its members and allow them input into this process through the democratic structure of the union.

Evidence will be submitted to the 'review body' which is most likely to be in the form of a pay claim for that year, together with the justification for this, e.g., the cost of living and the need to recruit more staff. The management side and the Government will also submit evidence and the 'review body' will make its recommendations, having consid-ered all submissions. The Government of the day will normally accept these recommendations.

However, there has been controversy with both Conservative and Labour Governments who, on separate occasions, did accept the recommendations, but insisted on the rise being phased. This has called into question the independence of the 'review body'.

Scrutinising Developments in the NHS

UNISON also takes an interest in issues that concern the NHS in general, since these may also affect their members' working conditions. For example, it has been one of the most vociferous critics of the Private Finance Initiative (PFI). It has held media conferences, issued leaflets and held meetings for members and for the general public on this issue.

UNISON also enters the world of politics as part of its function of protecting members' rights and interests. In 1998, it published a lengthy commentary on the announcement by the Chancellor of extra spending on the NHS.

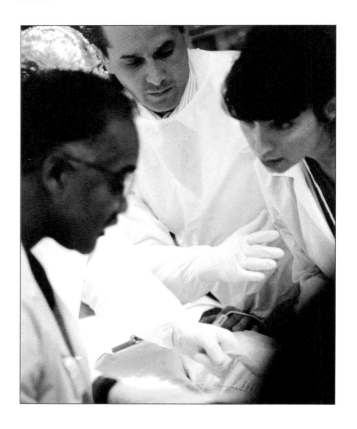

UNISON is also the largest trade union affiliated to the Trades Union Congress (TUC), its Scottish branch, the STUC, and the Labour Party. Its relationship particularly with the latter gives it an input into public policy and an influence on the Party and the Government. Although the present Government does not encourage close relations with the unions as much as its Labour predecessors, the formal relationship still affords unions some influence and UNISON will make use of this process.

Professional Associations

The British Medical Association (BMA)

Protecting Pay and Conditions

The BMA is, in effect, the trade union for doctors, of whom three-quarters are members. As such, it will represent collectively its members in various ways, as would any trade union. One of its most important functions will be the submission of evidence to the pay review body for doctors. It also has 'craft committees' which negotiate for the particular interests of each branch of the profession – junior doctors, hospital consultants, doctors specialising in public health and general practitioners.

Maintaining and Developing the Standards of the Profession

However, as a professional association, the BMA has a broader remit than just protecting pay and conditions. Any profession possesses a body of knowledge from which it derives skills and expertise. Those who wish to practise these are subject to a framework of licensing, where only those sufficiently qualified are allowed to do so and only after a lengthy period of approved study and training.

The BMA takes seriously its role as a representative of the profession. It issues press releases on matters affecting the delivery of health care and will make detailed submissions on the effects of government policies on the NHS and will react to any proposals made by the Government. Since it speaks with the authority of a professional association, its statements are taken seriously by both the public and the Government, although, obviously, all final decisions about the NHS are made by the democratically elected and accountable Government.

BMA in Action

In 1998, the BMA made representations to the Government on its proposals to reorganise the NHS, emphasising the necessity of direct GP input into the planning and management of the new Primary Care Trusts and into decisions over the financing of these.

The BMA also gave written and oral evidence to the Royal Commission on Long Term Care for the Elderly and to the Government's Review of Acute Services in Scotland.

The BMA has a Health Policy and Economic Research Unit which provides statistical and other information to support its submissions. Along with its recognised authority as the representative of its profession and its knowledge, this research and statistical backup gives the arguments of the BMA great weight in its dealings with the Government.

The General Medical Council (GMC)

The GMC is a statutory body, established by the Medical Act of 1858, to maintain a register of doctors and to regulate the fitness of doctors to practise. This gives it the responsibility of deciding who is fit to be included on the register in the first place, i.e., it has the right to approve, or otherwise, courses which lead to qualification as a doctor. This allows it some control of entry to the profession. It is an effective weapon against any dilution of the profession by, for example, a government which might wish to increase the number of doctors by lowering entry requirements to, or shortening, university medicine degree courses. Given its composition of mainly doctors, the GMC is sometimes seen by its critics as a body which protects the interests of the profession against those of the patient or society in general. However, it has also a disciplinary function and can investigate complaints of serious professional misconduct of doctors from the police, the public, the NHS and from other doctors. Doctors found guilty can be suspended or removed from the register, i.e., effectively prevented them from practising medicine.

The Royal Colleges

There are several Royal Colleges, e.g., the Royal College of Physicians and the Royal College of Surgeons. As their names suggest, they were established by Royal Charter, some of them hundreds of years ago. Their main responsibility is to train and examine postgraduate students within certain specialisms of the profession, e.g., surgeons. Like the BMA, they are in regular contact with the Government's Health Departments and put forward their views on a range of issues, particularly on official bodies like the Joint Consultants' Committee and the Standing Medical Advisory Committee.

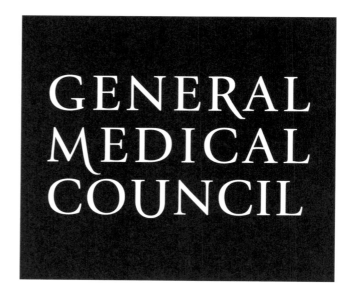

Setting the Agenda

The Royal Colleges have become involved in the politics of health in recent years, contributing to debate and sometimes setting the agenda. It was the Royal College of Physicians, for instance, which began publicising in the 1960s the dangers to health of smoking.

Several Royal Colleges have also been involved in the creation of anti-tobacco and anti-alcohol pressure groups. In 1998, the Royal College of Physicians of Edinburgh published a report which criticised the Scottish Office's own report on coronary heart disease in Scotland and, as a result, the Government revised its proposals.

Also in 1998, the Royal College of Physicians of Edinburgh, in partnership with the Royal College of Physicians and Surgeons of Glasgow, published a report on acute admissions to hospitals and how doctors' training may have to change to accommodate these.

The Colleges are, officially, non-political, but, because of the body of knowledge and expertise which they represent, they are very influential in the formation of public opinion and government policy.

Charities

There are many charities which have an interest in health care. However, there are two, in particular, whose views are important, because of the increasing numbers of elderly and very elderly people in the population and the implications of this for the NHS - Help the Aged and Age Concern.

In 1997, Help the Aged published a report, 'A Life Worth Living', on the independence and inclusion of older people. This was a comprehensive set of recommendations on how to help elderly people to participate more in society. It covered all relevant services including health care and 'Care in the Community'. Its publication in an election year ensured that all political parties had, at least, to be seen to be listening and taking the proposals seriously.

In 1997, Age Concern launched its 'Millennium Debate of the Age'. This consisted of seeking the views of individuals, private companies and public bodies on five issues, one being 'health and care'. The process also included commissioning reports drawn up by committees of people recognised as experts on each issue and using the information gathered. The end product, after debate and public feedback, was to publish in the spring of 2000 recommendations for future priorities, to be presented to the Government in 'The Agenda for the Age'.

Patients

In the late twentieth century, it became popular to regard patients as consumers of health care with rights, as well as being simply ill people and passive objects of care. There are several opportunities for people to express concerns or opinions on the NHS, either as individuals or collectively.

Health Councils

Health boards carry out surveys of public opinion on the delivery of services in their area. Each health board area has also a local health council which is designed to represent the interests of patients and draws its membership from individuals and groups in the area. It attempts to ascertain the opinions of the public on all areas of health care, e.g., the future of hospital provision, and passes these on to the health board. There are also complaints procedures which each health board must establish and make known to patients. Complaints about GPs can be made to the practice manager in the surgery, to the health board and, in some cases, to the General Medical Council.

Community Councils

Outwith the structure of the NHS and the medical profession, there are other means for people to participate in public discussion of health care policy. Community councils are consulted by health boards on their proposals for the delivery of health care and they are invited to nominate people for places on the local health council. They may also become involved in some local campaign related to the NHS, e.g., to oppose a hospital closure or to request the establishment of a pharmacy in their area.

Other Pressure Groups

The Patients' Association is a voluntary pressure group which campaigns across a broad range of issues affecting patients, e.g., funding of the NHS or the length of waiting lists. There are also pressure groups with specific interests, such as the Multiple Sclerosis Society. The Consumers' Association, which in the past concerned itself with identifying 'best buys' in consumer goods or in publicising bad practices by manufacturers and retailers in its monthly magazine, *Which?*, now has regular reports on aspects of health care – not just on obvious aspects, such as the best package of 'private medical insurance' available, but also on matters like the comparison between the length of waiting lists in different areas.

It should also not be forgotten that, in a democracy like Britain, where health care is regarded as a responsibility of government, the crucial role as a consumer that a citizen can play is in deciding who shall provide that commodity, i.e., in casting a vote in a general election.

Opinion Polls and General Elections

As an important political issue, the NHS is often the subject of opinion polls, especially during election campaigns. The results of these can provide some interesting indicators about the public's attitude to the NHS. During the 1992 General Election campaign, in a Gallup poll in the Telegraph, Labour had a 29% lead over the Conservatives as the party which would handle the NHS best. It also showed that 28% of all voters and 24% of Conservative voters felt that public services like the NHS had been cut too much under the Conservatives. However, the Conservatives went on to win the 1992 General Election with 41.9% of the vote, compared to Labour's 34.4%, and with an overall majority

of 21. During the 1997 General Election campaign in another Gallup poll in the same newspaper, 85% felt that, if the Tories won again, the NHS might no longer be a good service available to all. 64% also feared that, if Labour won, taxes might go up and people would be squeezed financially, although Labour was still regarded as the party best able to handle the NHS. At the actual election in 1997, Labour won 44.4% of the votes, compared to the Conservatives' 31.3%, and with an overall majority of 179.

From this, it could be argued that, although people consider the NHS (along with taxation) as an important electoral issue, it is not necessarily the only issue which will decide how they will vote. One might also question just how important the NHS is to voters if their perception of how well the parties would handle the NHS was scarcely different in these two elections and yet the actual results differed greatly. However, it should be noted that, in no election since 1945, have voters been presented with a clear choice of two major parties, one supporting the NHS and the other opposed. Therefore, it is impossible to gauge what the reaction of voters in electoral terms might be if a party stood for the abolition of free state-provided health care. It could be argued that voters have never had this choice because no major party would offer it, for fear of losing massive support, and that this is further evidence of how entrenched an institution the NHS has become in British politics.

In 1998, in a MORI survey for the BBC, 78% of Scots said they were satisfied with the health service, although 61% believed it to be underfunded and 62% were prepared to pay an extra 2p in the pound income tax towards improving the NHS, a power which the Scottish Parliament would be able to exercise. It will be interesting to see if any party proposes such an increase in future elections to the Scottish Parliament and what the reaction of Scottish voters would be.